ADVANTAGE Reading

Grade 5

Table of Contents

Table of Contents

CREDITS

Concept Development: Kent Publishing Services, Inc.

Written by: Roxanne Dorrie

Editor: Carla Hamaguchi

Designer/Production: Moonhee Pak/Mary Gagné

Illustrators: Frank Ordaz and Corbin Hillam

Art Director: Tom Cochrane

Project Director: Carolea Williams

Introduction

The Advantage Reading Series for grades 3–6 is shaped and influenced by current research findings in literacy instruction grounded in the federally mandated *No Child Left Behind* Act. It includes the following key skill strands:
- phonics/structural word analysis
- vocabulary development
- reading fluency
- reading comprehension

This series offers strong skill instruction along with motivational features in an easy-to-use format.

Take a look at all the advantages this reading series offers . . .

Phonics/Structural Word Analysis

Word analysis activities include the study of word syllabication, prefixes, suffixes, synonyms, antonyms, word roots, similes, metaphors, idioms, adjectives, adverbs, and much more. Word analysis helps students increase their **vocabulary, word-recognition skills,** and **spelling skills.**

Variety of Reading Genres

Fiction and Nonfiction

Students will have many opportunities to build reading skills by reading a variety of fiction, nonfiction, and poetry selections created in a **variety of visual formats** to simulate authentic reading styles. Each story selection builds on content vocabulary and skills introduced in the section. Fiction selections include fantasy, legends, realistic fiction, first-person narratives, and poetry. Nonfiction selections include biographies, how-to's, reports, and directions.

Graphic Information

Graphic information reading selections include charts, graphs, labels, maps, diagrams, and recipes. These types of reading opportunities help students hone **real-life reading** skills.

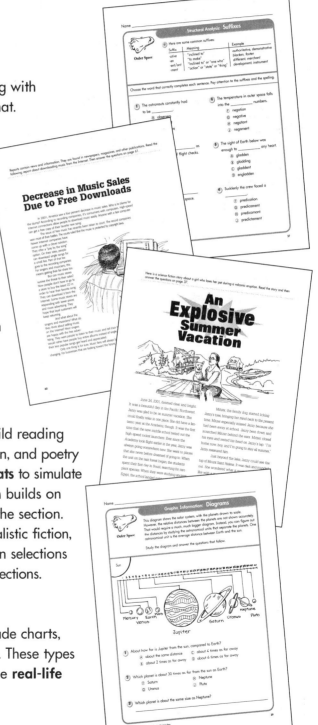

3

Comprehension Strategies

Strategic comprehension activities encourage students to make connections, ask questions, make predictions, and think about strategies they can use to **increase their understanding** of the text's meaning.

Fluency Practice

Reading fluency is the ability to **read with expression,** intonation, and a natural flow that sounds like talking. Fluency is essential for comprehension because the lack of it results in choppy, robotic reading that stands in the way of making sense out of a phrase or sentence.

Writing

Reading and writing are partner skills. A **range of writing activities** helps students improve their ability to write as well as learn about different forms of writing, such as signs, notes, personal narratives, riddles, poems, descriptions, journals, stories, and friendly letters.

Extensions and Real-Life Applications

Each unit ends with a "More Things to Do" page that includes suggestions for **hands-on experiences** that extend the theme. A list of books is also included for further study and enjoyment of the unit's theme.

Answer Key

Answers for each page are provided at the back of the book to make **checking answers quick and easy.**

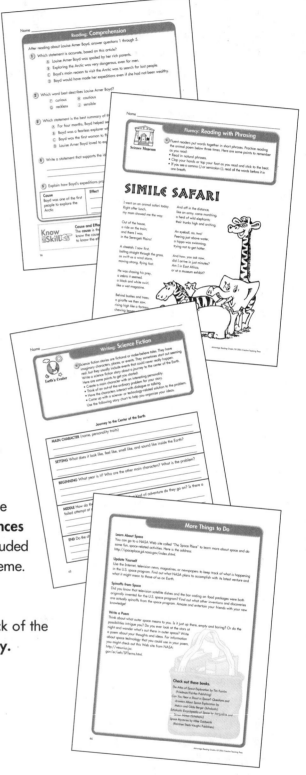

Comprehension: Prior Knowledge

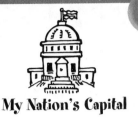

My Nation's Capital

Washington, D.C., is the capital of the United States of America. It is home to the White House, where the president lives. The president is responsible for making many important decisions, but he alone does not control the government. He heads the Executive Branch, one of the three branches of government that run our country.

Describe what you know about the president's job. Also describe what you know about the other branches of government.

Three Branches of Government

Legislative

_____
_____
_____
_____

Executive

President of the United States
_____
_____
_____

Judicial

_____
_____
_____
_____

Structural Analysis: **Syllables**

My Nation's Capital

⭐ A *syllable* is a group of letters that has a single vowel sound.
A two-syllable word has two vowel sounds.

One-Syllable Words	Two-Syllable Words
car	nap + kin = napkin
deck	pen + cil = pencil
dish	pic + nic = picnic
cot	pop + corn = popcorn
turn	nut + meg = nutmeg

Combine these syllables to make two-syllable words.

1   wit + ness = _____

2   pump + kin = _____

3   in + spect = _____

4   ship + ment = _____

5   plas + tic = _____

6   com + plete = _____

7   tad + pole = _____

8   vam + pire = _____

9   tar + nish = _____

10   bliss + ful = _____

Three-syllable words have three vowel sounds. Combine these syllables to make three-syllable words.

11   ar + gu + ment = _____

12   af + ter + noon = _____

13   com + pen + sate = _____

14   mem + or + ize = _____

15   max + i + mize = _____

Structural Analysis: VC/CV Syllabication Rule

My Nation's Capital

⭐ When two consonants stand between two vowels, divide the word between the consonants: com/mon, sub/ject. The vowel sound in the first syllable is usually short. Words that have double consonants also follow the VC/CV rule. They are divided between the double consonants: hap/pen, bon/net.

Divide these words into syllables using the VC/CV rule. Then write their syllable parts on the lines. The first one is done as an example.

	First Syllable	Second Syllable
1 hundred	hun / dred
2 children	_____ / _____
3 sample	_____ / _____
4 discuss	_____ / _____
5 sandwich	_____ / _____

Divide these double consonant words into syllables using the VC/CV rule. Then write their syllable parts on the lines. The first one is done as an example.

	First Syllable	Second Syllable
6 bottom	bot / tom
7 flannel	_____ / _____
8 annex	_____ / _____
9 cotton	_____ / _____
10 sudden	_____ / _____

Structural Analysis: **Multiple Syllables**

My Nation's Capital

⭐ Divide these words into their syllable parts by drawing one or more slashes through each word. Then write the syllables on the lines under the correct category. The first one is done as an example.

sig/nal	basket	magnet	important	garlic
fantastic	zipper	person	consent	illustrate
contest	interrupt	public	goblet	pancake
absent	until	carpenter	mutter	informal

Two-Syllable Words

1 _____sig_____ / _____nal_____

2 _____ / _____

3 _____ / _____

4 _____ / _____

5 _____ / _____

6 _____ / _____

7 _____ / _____

8 _____ / _____

9 _____ / _____

10 _____ / _____

11 _____ / _____

12 _____ / _____

13 _____ / _____

14 _____ / _____

Three-Syllable Words

15 _____ / _____ / _____

16 _____ / _____ / _____

17 _____ / _____ / _____

18 _____ / _____ / _____

19 _____ / _____ / _____

20 _____ / _____ / _____

Advantage Reading Grade 5 © 2004 Creative Teaching Press

Structural Analysis: **Word Building**

My Nation's Capital

Match the syllables to make a two-syllable word. Then write it on the line. The first one is done as an example.

kid — dom
     let
     nap   **1** __Kidnap__

ver dict
     port
     ber   **3** _____

cac den
     tus
     nal   **2** _____

chap mal
      bit
      ter   **4** _____

Reorder the syllables to make a three-syllable word. Then write it on the line.

5	lish	es	tab	_____
6	pen	tur	tine	_____
7	dif	ent	fer	_____
8	in	fere	ter	_____

Fill in the missing double consonants and write the words on the lines.

9	comes in the mail	le _ _ er	_____
10	what a horse does	ga _ _ op	_____
11	the top floor of a house	a _ _ ic	_____
12	game played with racquets	te _ _ is	_____
13	breakfast food	mu _ _ in	_____
14	baby cat	ki _ _ en	_____
15	fastens a shirt	bu _ _ on	_____
16	an old bone	fo _ _ il	_____
17	four quarts	ga _ _ on	_____

Fluency: **Reading with Expression**

My Nation's Capital

⭐ In 1963, Martin Luther King, Jr. delivered his "I Have a Dream" speech in Washington, D.C. Below is a part of that famous speech. Practice reading it three times. Then perform it for a friend. Here are some things for you to think about as you practice:

- Pause at commas.
- Read loudly and clearly.
- Use a commanding tone of voice.
- Vary your pace of speaking, slowing to stress key points.
- Ask for help with the pronunciation of tricky words.

"I say to you today, my friends, that in spite of the difficulties and frustrations of the moment, I still have a dream. It is a dream deeply rooted in the American dream.

I have a dream that one day this nation will rise up and live out the true meaning of its creed: 'We hold these truths to be self-evident: that all men are created equal.'

I have a dream that one day on the red hills of Georgia the sons of former slaves and the sons of former slaveowners will be able to sit down together at a table of brotherhood.

I have a dream that one day even the state of Mississippi, a desert state, sweltering with the heat of injustice and oppression, will be transformed into an oasis of freedom and justice.

I have a dream that my four children will one day live in a nation where they will not be judged by the color of their skin but by the content of their character.

I have a dream today."

Reading: **Comprehension**

Some pieces of writing express a point of view. A point of view is an author's opinion or idea about a subject. A reader can infer or figure out what the author's point of view is by paying close attention to the written message.

1 Reread the "I Have a Dream" speech on page 10. Choose a section that you think reveals the author's main message. Copy it onto the lines below.

_____

_____

_____

2 What does the section you just copied mean? What is the opinion expressed by the author?

_____

_____

_____

3 What is Martin Luther King's dream for America? Write your ideas below.

Name _____

My Nation's Capital

Vocabulary: Frequently Misused Words

⭐ Some verbs are often confused with similar sounding verbs. However, they cannot be used in the same way. The verb *lay* must have a direct object to complete the action. The verb *lie* is not followed by a direct object. Study the rules and examples below to better understand the differences between *lay* and *lie*.

LAY

Definition: to put something down   **Rule:** *usually* followed by a direct object

Present Tense: The umpire is laying the bases on the baseball field.

Past Tense: I laid the homework on her desk.

Past Participle: Sue has laid the bills on the table.

LIE

Definition: to recline or rest   **Rule:** *never* followed by a direct object

Present Tense: Each Friday the children lie down on their cots.

Past Tense: Yesterday the baby lay down on her back.

Past Participle: My dad has lain on the grass for a nap.

Write the correct word on the line to complete each sentence.

1   The book _____ overnight on the table.
        (laid, lay)

2   Deb _____ her red skirt out for the party.
        (has laid, has lain)

3   A lumberjack knows the direction that a fallen tree will _____.
        (lay, lie)

4   Tim _____ in bed all day.
        (has lain, has laid)

5   I _____ my cup on the saucer.
        (lay, laid)

6   Look at how carefully the dog _____ its bone in the ditch.
        (is lying, is laying)

Vocabulary: Content Words

My Nation's Capital

Here are some common words about the U.S. government. Memorize their definitions.

bill	suggestion for a law
citizen	a person who belongs to a particular country
Constitution	the document that states the basic principles of American government
immigrant	a person who moves into a country
politician	someone who works in politics, such as a governor or a senator
veto	to cancel or postpone a bill

Choose a word from above to complete the sentences.

1. The _____ was almost passed in Congress.

2. She decided she would run for office and become a _____.

3. My father is an _____ who left his native country many years ago.

4. He became a _____ of the country after living here for over twenty years.

5. The president wanted to _____ the new law because it would create more taxes.

Locate and circle the government words in the puzzle below. The words can be found in a straight line going across or up and down.

```
V A P I M M I G R A N T T O S C T I O N
I M O B I L I B C E W I N S O T P A G E
G V D H I P O L I T I C I A N T H O B I
C E T I C O N S T I T U T I O N T E I O
R T S T I O N M I A G R A N T O P I L V
L O Z E N L A P Z E M B I O P L A C L T
H O V E O T I Z E N M S P A F S H I N G
G R E A H M E N N E T R O B L B E N E L
```

This is a short biography about the life of Eleanor Roosevelt, wife of the 32nd U.S. president, Franklin Roosevelt. Read the biography and then answer the questions on page 15.

ELEANOR Roosevelt

Eleanor Roosevelt was born in New York City on October 11, 1884. Her mother died when she was eight. Her father died when she was ten. Eleanor went to live with her grandmother. She later lived at a boarding school in England. Upon her return home, Eleanor met and fell in love with her distant cousin, Franklin Roosevelt. They were married in 1903 and over the next 11 years, Eleanor gave birth to six children.

Eleanor devoted herself to others, including her husband. When Franklin suffered from polio and could no longer walk on his own, she gave him strength. Her support helped him throughout his career. It helped him get all the way to the presidency in 1933.

Eleanor brought her ideas and dreams to the White House. She changed the role of the First Lady. She still gave parties, but she also worked to make life better for people all over the world. She set up a school for poor children. She helped create UNICEF, a fund that helps feed and take care of children who are living in poverty and war-torn places.

Eleanor spoke up about the issues she cared about. She was the first president's wife to hold her own press conferences. She gave speeches and talked on the radio. She even wrote a daily newspaper column called "My Way."

Eleanor later took on her biggest and greatest goal: to make people aware that everyone has basic human rights and freedoms. She helped to put this in writing. The Universal Declaration of Human Rights was written in many languages. Eleanor spread this message all over the world until the day she died. She died in 1962 and was buried next to her husband in New York.

Eleanor Roosevelt made a difference in the world. Her life reflected the words she once said: "You get more joy out of giving to others, and should put a good deal of thought into the happiness you are able to give."

Advantage Reading Grade 5 © 2004 Creative Teaching Press

Name _____

Reading: Comprehension

Fill in the bubble next to the correct answer.

1 When did Eleanor Roosevelt set up a school for poor children?

    Ⓐ in 1903   Ⓒ before she got married

    Ⓑ when her father died   Ⓓ after she moved into the White House

2 What happened first?

    Ⓕ Eleanor's mother died.   Ⓗ Eleanor met Franklin Roosevelt.

    Ⓖ Eleanor helped create UNICEF.   Ⓙ Eleanor went to boarding school.

3 What happened last?

    Ⓐ Eleanor helped create UNICEF.

    Ⓑ Eleanor gave birth to six children.

    Ⓒ Eleanor set up a school for poor children.

    Ⓓ Eleanor spread the message about human rights.

4 Which of these sentences expresses an opinion?

    Ⓕ Eleanor went to live with her grandmother.

    Ⓖ Eleanor spoke up about the issues she cared about.

    Ⓗ She was the first president's wife to hold her own press conferences.

    Ⓙ You should put a good deal of thought into the happiness you are able to give.

5 Which of these is a fact?

    Ⓐ She changed the role of the First Lady.

    Ⓑ You get more joy out of giving to others.

    Ⓒ She gave speeches and talked on the radio.

    Ⓓ Her support helped her husband throughout his career.

Know THE Skill

Fact vs. Opinion
Facts are true. Opinions are not always true. They are personal views or beliefs. To tell the difference between a fact and an opinion, ask yourself, "Would everyone agree that this is true?"

Here is a story about a boy's field trip to Washington, D.C. Read the story and then answer the questions on page 19.

Lost in D.C.

Last week, I went to Washington, D.C. Every year, the sixth grade visits the White House and a bunch of other government buildings. Before we left, our teacher, Mr. Daves, told us that what we learned this year would help us understand the history behind the places we'd see. He said the field trip would **knock our socks off.** I wasn't so sure I would remember much since history was usually my time to **catch some Zs.**

D.C. was a really busy place. There were cars and big buildings everywhere. On the first day of the field trip, it was **raining cats and dogs** so we spent the whole day in museums. My favorite was the Natural History Museum. It was a treasure house full of plants, animals, rocks, fossils, and artifacts.

The following day was sunny and warm so we saw all sorts of people. There were mothers pushing their babies in strollers. There were men and women dressed in business suits and sneakers walking together, **shooting the breeze.** There were lots of kids from other schools on field trips, too. I don't remember the last time I saw so many people in one place. **It made my head spin.**

Our walking tour started at the Capitol. It was enormous! Then we followed Mr. Daves to the Botanic Gardens. He told us to prepare for a full day of exercise. So far, I thought it was a **piece of cake;** no boring lectures to listen to and no tests to take. I had no idea of the adventure that was ahead of me.

After posing for a class picture, we all took a short break in the Botanic Gardens. Some kids rested on the benches. Some of us went to get up close to a statue in the shape of an empty cube. That's when Mr. Daves called us over to continue the tour. I didn't think he'd get **bent out of shape** if I quickly walked inside the cube. It was like a tunnel inside.

On the other side, I noticed a gardener struggling to yank out a big weed. It must have had strong roots because he was pulling hard. I went over to **lend a hand.** Just then it popped out. He looked up at me and said, "I sure needed a lot of **elbow grease** for that one!"

We got into a conversation and I told him where I was from and that I thought the Capitol was as big as my school. I think he must have overheard many tour guides because he seemed to know more about Washington, D.C., than Mr. Daves. He said that the Capitol had been burned by British troops in 1814 and rebuilt the following year. I imagined the building ablaze and the glow lighting up the streets like a bonfire.

When I turned to see what direction the class had taken, I realized they were gone! I was about to start running until I suddenly remembered that Mr. Daves said the tour would end at the White House. I asked the gardener for directions. He pointed to a tall, pencil-shaped building in the distance and said to go straight until I reached it. He said it was called the Washington Monument. He continued by telling me to notice the color difference halfway up the building. It marked the place where construction had stopped because of a lack of funds due to the Civil War. The gardener said to take a right at the monument and I would see the White House across the street.

As I began to run, I could hear him in the distance shouting, "Believe it or not, the White House was also burned to the ground by the same British troops who burned the Capitol!" **I put my pedal to the metal** and went as fast as my legs would take me.

I ran past the museums that we visited the day before. I looked around to see if I could recognize any familiar faces. I continued to run and before I knew it, I was at the Washington Monument. I saw my class at the base of it. They were staring up at the strange, tall building. They were listening intently to Mr. Daves and nobody even seemed to realize that I was missing. I stopped to take a breath and think. **I thought fast on my feet** and came up with a plan. I decided to sneak up and pretend that I was standing there the whole time. The plan was working until Mr. Daves stopped in the middle of a sentence to give me a puzzled look. He must have noticed that I was sweating and panting. I tried to look alert even though I felt **run-down.** He was about to say something to me when I quickly offered these words: "Did you know that the Washington Monument was only halfway built because of the Civil War?" I pointed to it. "Look, you can see where it changes color!"

All of a sudden, everyone seemed less interested in me. Their heads all turned to try and see where the color of the monument changed from light grey to dark grey. Mr. Daves looked surprised. He said to me, "I guess you really have been listening during history class." I sighed in relief. I was **off the hook.** Then I thought to myself, "Just wait until he finds out what I know about the White House!"

Advantage Reading Grade 5 © 2004 Creative Teaching Press

Reading: **Comprehension**

Fill in the bubble next to the correct answer.

1 In what kind of setting does the story most likely take place?

Ⓐ a city

Ⓑ a farm

Ⓒ a park

Ⓓ a playground

Write the letter of the correct meaning on the line next to each idiom.

2 _____ knock one's socks off

3 _____ catch some Zs

4 _____ raining cats and dogs

5 _____ shoot the breeze

6 _____ make one's head spin

7 _____ piece of cake

8 _____ bent out of shape

9 _____ lend a hand

10 _____ elbow grease

11 _____ put one's pedal to the metal

12 _____ thinking fast on one's feet

13 _____ run-down

14 _____ off the hook

A quick to think of ideas

B make casual conversation

C sleep for a while; take a nap

D become surprised and excited

E very easy

F in poor condition; very tired

G help out

H hurry up; go fast

I no longer in trouble

J upset; angry

K raining very hard

L feeling confused

M hard work; effort

Defining Idioms
Idioms are figures of speech or popular phrases used when speaking. Idioms are not literal. They do not mean exactly what the words convey. For example, when people say "Break a leg!" they don't really want the person to get hurt. The idiom "Break a leg" means "Good luck."

Name _____

My Nation's Capital

Study the chart below. Then read the following paragraphs about how the three branches of government work. Copy information from the chart onto the blank lines in the paragraphs below.

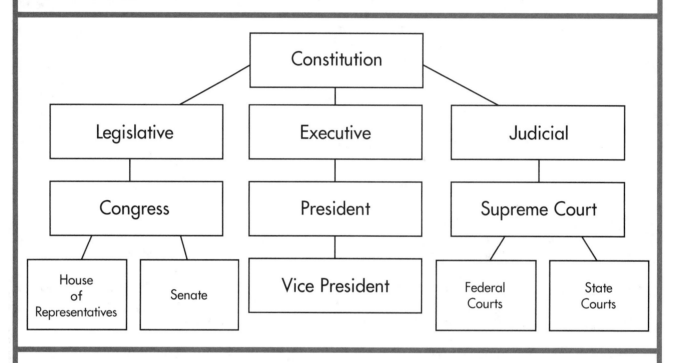

The _____ of the United States was written in 1787. Its laws help to define the parts of government and their specific powers. It is sometimes called a system of checks and balances because it makes sure that no one branch of government can dominate or have power over the other two.

The Legislative Branch is run by _____, which is divided into two parts, the _____ and the _____. Some of their other powers include passing laws and coming up with ideas for how to spend money.

The Executive Branch is led by the _____. He directs the government and is the main leader. Some of his powers include commanding the armed forces and thinking of new laws. The _____ is second in command. He must be ready to take over if the _____ dies, is fired, or is not able to do the job.

The Judicial Branch is headed by the _____. Its main role is to interpret laws of the _____. Cases that are heard there are ones that were first heard at the lower level courts, the _____ and the _____.

Name _____

My Nation's Capital

Writing: **Persuasive Essays**

⭐ In persuasive writing, the author tries to persuade or convince readers to agree with a particular opinion or point of view.

In order to write a strong persuasive essay, remember to:
• Choose your position. What do you want to convince readers of?
• Support your position with three solid reasons.
• Support the reasons with examples, facts, and evidence.
• Briefly restate your position and your most compelling reason in your conclusion.

Write a persuasive essay about a particular right or responsibility that American citizens have. Choose from the topic ideas below or write your own on the line provided.

Topic 1   American children have the right to have an education.

Topic 2   Americans have the responsibility to recycle.

My Topic   _____

Plan Your Position

I think _____
_____

Reason #1	Examples, Facts, Evidence
_____	_____
_____	_____

Reason #2	Examples, Facts, Evidence
_____	_____
_____	_____

Reason #3	Examples, Facts, Evidence
_____	_____
_____	_____

Conclusion _____
_____

Name _____

My Nation's Capital

⭐ Write your persuasive essay on the lines. Use the graphic organizer on page 21 to plan your writing.

_____

_____

_____

_____

_____

_____

_____

_____

_____

_____

_____

Read your essay, then ask yourself:
• Am I convincing?
• Will a reader understand my position and agree with my reasons?
Edit, correct, and rewrite the essay to improve it. Have a friend read it and respond to your argument. Summarize the friend's response on the lines below.

_____

_____

Word Practice

Make a list of compound words. Read the words and clap the syllables in them. See if the VC/CV rule applies to any of the words and, if so, divide them on paper. Get a dictionary and find as many words as you can that follow this pattern. Look for two- and three-syllable words.

Fluency Practice

Reread the speech on page 10. Notice how the writer repeats key phrases to keep the listeners interested. Write a short speech about fair play on the playground or in sports. Think of and repeat a key phrase to make your speech more powerful. Practice reading your speech with a strong voice, pausing at commas and varying the pace to empha-size key points. Deliver your speech to a group of friends.

Make a Collage about a Political Issue

Choose a current political issue such as a new law or an election. Research it by reading newspaper and magazine articles and searching the Internet. Keep track of it over a week. Cut out photos and articles about it. Paste them to a piece of poster board. Use a black marker to write phrases that state your position about the issue. Present the collage to your family and ask them to try to identify the issue and your position.

Check out these books.

American Statues and Monuments by Jill Foran (Weigl Publishers)

The Declaration of Independence by Dennis Brindell Fradin (Children's Book Press)

Hail to the Chief: The American Presidency by Don Robb (Charlesbridge Publishing)

Our Constitution by Linda Carlson Johnson (Millbrook Press)

A Patriotic Primer by Lynne Cheney (Simon & Schuster)

President Citizen by Toni Goffe (Child's Play)

The U.S. Capitol by Lola Schaefer (Heinemann Library)

Earth's Center

Comprehension: **Prior Knowledge**

Did you know that the Earth's continents and oceans make up only a thin crust that extends about 20 miles down? What lies below this layer? What would the Earth look like if you were to cut it in half? Draw your ideas below and label the sections with numbers. Then use the chart below the diagram to record your ideas and descriptions.

Earth Part   **Description**

	Earth Part	Description
1	Outer Crust _____	_____
		_____
2	_____	_____
		_____
3	_____	_____
		_____
4	_____	_____
		_____

Advantage Reading Grade 5 © 2004 Creative Teaching Press

Structural Analysis: **V/CV Syllabication Rule**

Earth's Center

⭐ When a single consonant stands between two vowels, the most common division is before the consonant: spi/der, ro/tate, a/gent. The vowel sound in the first syllable is usually long.

Divide these words into syllables using the V/CV rule. Then write their syllable parts on the lines. The first one is done as an example.

		First Syllable		Second Syllable
1	music	_mu_	/	_sic_
2	tulip	_____	/	_____
3	ivy	_____	/	_____
4	decide	_____	/	_____
5	bacon	_____	/	_____
6	paper	_____	/	_____
7	trophy	_____	/	_____

Use the words above to fill in the blanks and complete the sentences.

8 John is allergic to poison _____.

9 My favorite breakfast is eggs and _____.

10 Mary won a _____ for coming in first place.

11 The most beautiful flower in his garden is the red _____.

12 She used a large piece of _____ for her painting.

13 It is time to _____ what to wear for the party.

Earth's Center

Structural Analysis: VC/V Syllabication Rule

⭐ When a single consonant stands between two vowels, divide it using the VC/V rule if the word has a short vowel sound for the first syllable. Here are some examples: trav/el, cop/y, vol/ume.

Divide these words into syllables using the VC/V rule. Then write their syllable parts on the lines.

First Syllable   Second Syllable

1 camel ___cam___ / ___el___

2 menu _____ / _____

3 finish _____ / _____

4 lemon _____ / _____

5 study _____ / _____

6 novel _____ / _____

Use the words above to fill in the blanks and complete the sentences.

7 He looked at the _____ before ordering a meal.

8 I am in the middle of reading my favorite _____.

9 Squeeze a _____ into the pitcher when you make ice tea.

10 When will you plan to _____ doing the laundry?

11 She plans to _____ all night for the test.

12 I count only one hump on the back of that _____.

Advantage Reading Grade 5 © 2004 Creative Teaching Press

Structural Analysis: V/CV and VC/V Syllabication Rule

Earth's Center

⭐ Decide whether to divide the following words before the consonant (V/CV rule) or after it (VC/V rule). Divide and then pronounce the word as you write it under the correct heading. Mark the first vowel long (ō) or short (ô).

polish	radish	punish	vital
polo	level	pony	tonic
metal	legal	relish	total
meter	bonus	recent	vacant
raven	body	vivid	vanish

V/CV

1. ___pō___ / ___lo___
2. _____ / _____
3. _____ / _____
4. _____ / _____
5. _____ / _____
6. _____ / _____
7. _____ / _____
8. _____ / _____
9. _____ / _____
10. _____ / _____

VC/V

11. ___pôl___ / ___ish___
12. _____ / _____
13. _____ / _____
14. _____ / _____
15. _____ / _____
16. _____ / _____
17. _____ / _____
18. _____ / _____
19. _____ / _____
20. _____ / _____

Structural Analysis: Word Building

Earth's Center

⭐ Choose words from the box to use in place of the underlined words. Write the correct word on the line at the end of each sentence. Then complete the crossword puzzle using the words. V/CV words go down. VC/V words go across.

sinus	raven	punish	clever
credit	present	student	spider

V/CV DOWN

1. We had to <u>scold, discipline</u> the dog because he turned over the trash can. _____

2. I got the best <u>gift</u> for my birthday this year. _____

3. She deserves most of the <u>praise, approval</u> because it was her idea. _____

4. The <u>smart, skillful</u> magician invented a trick to make a rabbit disappear. _____

VC/V ACROSS

5. The <u>black bird</u> flew up high into the treetops. _____

6. Yesterday I found a big, hairy <u>bug that spins webs</u> climbing up the side of the shed. _____

7. Tim was the first <u>pupil</u> to raise a hand when the teacher asked the question. _____

8. Every spring I feel <u>nasal opening in the skull</u> pressure because of my allergies. _____

Advantage Reading Grade 5 © 2004 Creative Teaching Press

Earth's Center

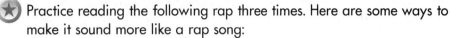

Fluency: Reading with Expression

⭐ Practice reading the following rap three times. Here are some ways to make it sound more like a rap song:
- Give yourself a beat (tap or clap).
- Try to read each phrase to the beat.
- Emphasize words in *italics*.

When you are ready, read the rap to a friend. Ask your friend to clap to the beat as you read.

Earth Rap

Paragraph 1
Our planet has more
than just oceans and land,
it's got a center part
with a great big span.
More than three thousand miles
below our feet,
lies the Earth's inner core,
radiating heat.

Paragraph 2
Think of the Earth
as a giant peach,
the skin's the outer crust,
but not good to eat;
Made of oceans
and soil
and mountains
and streams;
It makes *this* the only planet
we'd dare to live and dream.

Paragraph 3
Peel back the outer layer
and what's inside?
The meat of the peach,
it's the mantle, that's right!
Almost two thousand miles
thick all around,
It has slow-moving rock,
causing movement in the ground;
Known as continent drifting,
and ocean floor sinking,
I'm not waiting around
for the Earth to start shifting.

When the Earth's skin breaks,
it's not like a tornado,
it's the mantle popping up
in the form of a volcano.

Paragraph 4
Below the Earth's mantle,
lies the pit of the peach,
called the outer core,
about a thousand miles deep;
Made of liquid iron,
it's piping hot.
Would you go swimming there?
I *definitely* would not!

Paragraph 5
And last but not least,
is the seed of the pit,
the Earth's inner core,
its innermost bit.
It's a core within a core,
but not liquid at all;
The pressure all around
makes it hard like a brick wall.
It's the deepest part,
of the Earth's big belly.
It's the hottest part,
eight thousand degrees, *whoa* Nellie!

Paragraph 6
That's the Earth's story,
don't try and hide it
like a peach in your hand;
Now you know what's inside it.

When you compare and contrast two or more things, you tell what is the same and different about them. Compare and contrast the parts of the Earth described in "Earth Rap" on page 29. Fill in the chart with facts from the rap.

	Outer Crust	Mantle	Inner Core
Same			
Different			

1 What metaphor does the author use to compare the Earth in "Earth Rap"?

_____

2 What metaphor does the author use to compare the "outer crust" in paragraph 2?

_____

3 What metaphor does the author use to compare the "mantle" in paragraph 3?

_____

4 What metaphor does the author use to compare the "outer core" in paragraph 4?

_____

5 What metaphor does the author use to compare the "inner core" in paragraph 5?

_____

Know **the** **Skill**

Identifying Metaphors
A metaphor is a figure of speech that compares two otherwise unrelated things by saying that one is the other. Metaphors are often used in poems to create metal images. Here are some examples of metaphors:
- My heart *is* a singing bird.
- The sun *is* a yellow beach ball.
- Life *is* a parade.

   Advantage Reading Grade 5 © 2004 Creative Teaching Press

Earth's Center

Vocabulary: Frequently Misused Words

⭐ Sometimes a verb can be confused with a similar sounding verb. However, they cannot be used in the same way. The verb *set* must have a direct object to complete the action. The verb *sit* is not followed by a direct object. Study the charts below to better understand the differences between *set* and *sit*.

SET

Definition: to put or place something down **Rule:** *usually* followed by a direct object

Present Tense: Please <u>set</u> the money on the counter.

Past Tense: We <u>set</u> the dishes on the table.

Past Participle: He <u>has set</u> the hot dogs on the grill.

SIT

Definition: rest in a seated position **Rule:** *never* followed by a direct object

Present Tense: I like to <u>sit</u> on the soft couch.

Past Tense: The baby <u>sat</u> quietly in the high chair.

Past Participle: No one <u>has sat</u> on that bench for years.

Write the correct word on the line to complete each sentence.

1 Please _____ down and keep me company.
      (sit, set)

2 Last night, Tom _____ his cap on the desk.
      (sat, set)

3 That umbrella _____ on the floor since last week.
      (has set, has sat)

4 Linda _____ on the bleachers and waited for her mom.
      (sat, set)

5 Dave _____ the pencils in the jar.
      (has sat, has set)

6 Dad wants you to _____ the mail on the table.
      (set, sit)

Vocabulary: **Content Words**

Earth's Center

Here are some common geological words. Memorize their definitions.

core	the center part of the Earth
crater	a large, hollow, steep-sided depression on the Earth's surface
crust	the outer layer of rock around the Earth
erosion	what happens when ground wears away such as in a landslide or rockfall
eruption	what happens when solid, liquid, and gas are ejected from a volcano
fossil	any evidence of past life such as bones, animal parts, and imprints
geology	the study of Earth science
geothermal	heat from inside the Earth
glacier	a large mass of ice formed by compacted snow
lava	hot, liquid rock that erupts from a volcano
mantle	the part of the Earth that lies between the crust and the core
plate	one of the moving jigsaw pieces that makes up the Earth's crust

Locate and circle the geological words in the puzzle. The words can be found in a straight line going across or up and down.

```
P S P I R M A N T L E C E P S S A T G O N S L O P
K F O B I L I B C E W I N S O T P A L E T M A K O
G O D H I E R U P T I O N T H O C I L Y I S V R V
C S T C I E R S T L A V T I N T O E C O P L A T E
R S H T I O N M I A G E O T H E R M A L F S S I L
L I Z N L A P Z E M I R O P L I E K T O S T I O N
H L V E C T I Z E N M O P A F S H I R A G Y U T L
G E O L R A P H Y E I S O B L B E N G L A C I E R
H L I E U T I Z P N M I I A F S H Y O M O P I E R
A L V E S T A Z E G E O L O G Y H I R A G Y U F J
C G F X T D I S U N M N P A C R A T E R O N L S K
```

Here is a science fiction story about a girl who loses her pet during a volcanic eruption. Read the story and then answer the questions on page 37.

An Explosive Summer Vacation

June 24, 2301, dawned clear and bright. It was a beautiful day in the Pacific Northwest. Jazzy was glad to be on summer vacation. She could finally relax in one place. She did have a fantastic year at the Academy, though. It was the first time that the new middle school tested out the high-speed rocket launchers. Ever since the Academy took flight earlier in the year, Jazzy was always going somewhere new. She went to places that she never before dreamed of going to. When the unit on the rain forest began, the students spent their first day in Brazil, searching for rare plant species. When they were studying ancient Egypt, the school landed right next to a pyramid!

Mitzer, the family dog, started licking Jazzy's toes, bringing her mind back to the present time. Mitzer especially missed Jazzy because she had been away at school. Jazzy bent down and scratched Mitzer behind the ears. Mitzer closed his eyes and rested his head on Jazzy's lap. "I'm home now, boy, and I'm going to stay all summer," Jazzy reassured him.

Just beyond the lake, Jazzy could see the top of Mount Saint Helens. It was dark and rounded out. She wondered what it must have looked like with a snow-capped peak, before the eruption of 1980. She imagined it standing tall, green, and majestic, with a hint of white lacing the top.

Mount St. Helens was still green and alive; it had over 320 years to recover from its last eruption. But the huge 1980 blast swept away one entire side of the volcano, killing 57 people and countless animals.

"What would a real eruption be like?" Jazzy wondered. She looked down at Mitzer. He was sleeping peacefully. "At least we wouldn't be in any danger," she told him. All houses built in the 23rd century or later were equipped with rocket launchers. This made moving very easy for families. All they had to do was fly their home to a new location and park it there until the family was ready to move again. The residents in the towns surrounding Mount St. Helens didn't have anything to worry about. They were all ready to take off in a moment's notice.

Later that evening, around the dinner table, Jazzy was surprised by the conversation. Her earlier thoughts were the main topic of discussion. Her dad was telling the family about recent activity at the volcano. "People at work were talking about steam and smoke spraying out of the top," he reported. "On my flight home today, I noticed some black dust shooting right out of that crater at the top," he continued. "Do you think that the volcano is trying to tell us something?"

"Yeah," Jazzy turned to her dad. "I think that Mount St. Helens is trying to tell us she is ready for another big eruption!" She went on, "After all, the volcano hasn't had a big one for over 320 years."

"Well, if that happens, the whole town

will be evacuated. I just had the house rockets inspected. They are all working just fine." He looked into his daughter's worried eyes. "Don't worry, Jazzy. I'll have this house in the sky before the lava even starts to flow."

Just as her father had finished speaking, Jazzy felt the floor beneath her feet start to shake. "Mom! Dad!" she shouted. "Put on your safety belts everyone!" his voice trailed as he ran out of the room. Jazzy heard a crash and turned to see the dishes falling off the table, one by one. The shaking got stronger and louder. Then, BOOM! A huge explosion sounded! Jazzy

knew what to do. She quickly strapped herself into a sofa. Her mother did, too.

Soon, the house was zipping through the late evening sky. Jazzy looked out the big living room window. She could see other houses beginning to launch. She looked past the treetops to see Mount St. Helens fuming and spilling out ash, smoke, and lava. Outside, Jazzy could hear a loud siren signaling the residents to evacuate. She heard people yelling and dogs barking. "Oh no! Mitzer!" she cried. "Mom! We forgot Mitzer!"

"It's too late to turn back, Jazzy," her mother told her. "We might crash into another

What will happen next in the story? How do you think it will end? Write your predictions on the lines below.

_____

_____

_____

house if we spin around in this chaos. Or worse, we may not get out of here before the ash and smoke fill up the air and our lungs," she added. "It just isn't worth risking our lives. I'm sorry."

The words were painful to Jazzy's ears. She thought about Mitzer. He was old and would probably get lost in the confusion. Jazzy started to feel the tears well up in her eyes. She

from the top floor. "It's Mitzer!" shouted Jazzy. "He's upstairs!"

Jazzy darted up the staircase. Her parents followed her. Jazzy opened her bedroom door and there, wagging his tail wildly, was Mitzer. Jazzy threw her arms around the dog. "Mitzer! You're alive!" Jazzy turned to her parents and asked, "What do you think happened?"

didn't try to argue. Deep down inside, she knew her mother was right.

About an hour later, the house landed safely on a large field. Jazzy's father walked into the living room. "We're here!" he announced. "According to the radar, we should be just outside of Portland, Oregon."

"Dad," Jazzy said softly, "we left Mitzer behind." She got up to hug her father. She knew he would understand how she felt.

Just then, the sound of barking came

"From the looks of it," her mother said, "Mitzer found a pretty good hiding place during the eruption." Jazzy's mother pointed to the ruffled up bed covers. She continued, "When the house launched, the door must have shut, trapping Mitzer!"

"I'm just glad he's OK," Jazzy said. "Mom, Dad, this time can we please move to a place that doesn't have a volcano anywhere near it? I think Mitzer has had enough excitement for the rest of his life!"

Advantage Reading Grade 5 © 2004 Creative Teaching Press

Reading: **Comprehension**

A summary is a brief recap of a story. It tells the main ideas and actions. It does not go into detail. A summary usually includes a story's main character, setting, problem, and solution. Use the chart to write notes about the story. Then use the information to write a short summary.

MAIN CHARACTER (name, age, gender)

_____

_____

SETTING (location, important geographic information)

_____

_____

PROBLEM What is the main action? What is the problem?

_____

_____

SOLUTION How is the problem solved? How does the story end? Is there a message or moral?

_____

_____

Summary of *An Explosive Summer Vacation*

_____

_____

_____

_____

_____

_____

_____

_____

_____

A recount is a second telling of an event. Many newspaper articles are recounts. They describe an event that happened. Read this recount of one man's real experience witnessing the 1980 Mount St. Helens eruption.

Witness to the Mount St. Helens Eruption

John H. Lienhard thought that May 18, 1980, would be just another ordinary day. He got up and drove to the Pendleton, Oregon, airport to catch his first flight. He was on his way to Chicago. As the plane flew high above Mount St. Helens, the pilot told the passengers to look out their windows. He said that the volcano was making a "spectacular display."

John leaned over to look out of the closest window. He was amazed by what he witnessed. He said, "What had been a rather tranquil landscape only moments before had become an almost indescribable scene. A plume of black ash immediately exploded from the mountain and went straight up."

The plane landed at the Portland airport. John described the sky there as "not a clear blue that was evident before the eruption, but rather a hazy yellowish hue." He was surprised by the "certain odor in the air that might have been a sulfur smell."

On his next flight, John asked for a window seat to get the "best view." What he saw next was an amazing spectacle. "The mountain was belching ash and smoke and was very dark and eerie. There appeared to be lightning flashes coming from the crater." John also noticed that a giant cloud of ash seemed to be trailing behind the plane.

Upon his arrival in Chicago, John learned that he had been on one of the last planes that left Portland that day. He said he still has his airline tickets along with his "memories."

Advantage Reading Grade 5 © 2004 Creative Teaching Press

Reading: **Comprehension**

After reading *Witness to the Mount St. Helens Eruption* on page 38, answer question 1 through 4.

1 Why did the sky have a "hazy yellowish hue" and "sulfur smell" at the Portland airport?

_____

_____

2 Why did John keep his airline tickets?

_____

_____

3 Is *An Explosive Summer Vacation* (pages 33–36) fiction or nonfiction?

_____

What information from the story helped you to know whether it is fiction or nonfiction?

_____

_____

_____

4 Is *Witness to the Mount St. Helens Eruption* fiction or nonfiction? _____

What information from the story helped you to know whether it is fiction or nonfiction?

_____

_____

_____

Fiction vs. Nonfiction
What is the difference between fiction and nonfiction? Fictional writing is not true. Nonfiction writing is real or true.

Name _____

Earth's Center

Study the time line below. Use the information from the time line to answer questions 1 through 4.

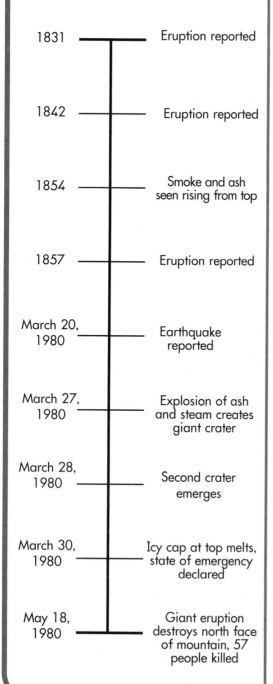

Recorded Volcanic Activity at Mount St. Helens

1831	Eruption reported
1842	Eruption reported
1854	Smoke and ash seen rising from top
1857	Eruption reported
March 20, 1980	Earthquake reported
March 27, 1980	Explosion of ash and steam creates giant crater
March 28, 1980	Second crater emerges
March 30, 1980	Icy cap at top melts, state of emergency declared
May 18, 1980	Giant eruption destroys north face of mountain, 57 people killed

1 In what year was the first recorded eruption at Mount St. Helens?

Ⓐ 1831

Ⓑ 1854

Ⓒ 1857

Ⓓ 1980

2 What happened in 1854?

Ⓕ A crater emerged.

Ⓖ Steam melted the icy cap.

Ⓗ Smoke and ash rose from the top.

Ⓙ The north side of the mountain was destroyed.

3 On what date in 1980 was a state of emergency declared?

Ⓐ March 20th

Ⓑ March 27th

Ⓒ March 28th

Ⓓ March 30th

4 What happened on May 18, 1980?

Ⓕ The icy snow cap melted.

Ⓖ An eruption killed 57 people.

Ⓗ A second giant crater emerged.

Ⓙ An earthquake created a crater at the top.

Graphic Information: **Diagrams**

Earth's Center

Diagrams show information in a picture format. They are useful in showing three-dimensional information such as objects, places, and buildings. Parts can be labeled and drawn in. Study the following diagram of the Earth's interior. Then read the paragraph and use information from the diagram to fill in the blank lines in the paragraph.

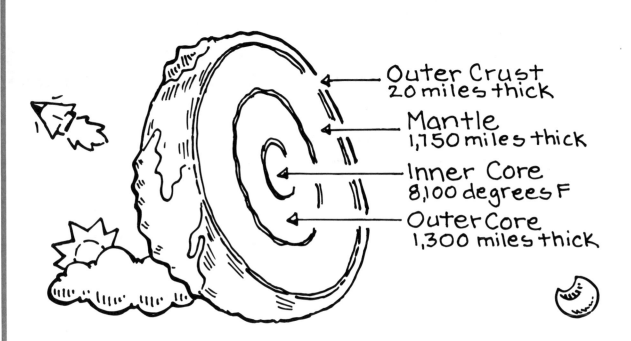

Outer Crust
20 miles thick

Mantle
1,750 miles thick

Inner Core
8,100 degrees F

Outer Core
1,300 miles thick

Planet _____ is made up of three main parts: the outer crust, the mantle, and the core.

The _____ is 20 miles thick. That is very thin compared to the other parts of the planet.

It is the only part that sustains life. It is made up of both continents and oceans. Underneath is the

_____, which is 1,750 miles thick. It is made of molten rock that slowly moves the sur-

face, causing continents to drift and areas of the ocean floor to shift. The core of the planet has

two main parts. The _____ is 1,300 miles thick. It is made of very hot liquid iron and

nickel. Further below that is the _____, which is also made up of iron and nickel. It is

solid and hard because of all the outside pressure. This innermost part of the planet is a scorching

8,100 degrees Fahrenheit!

Name _____

Earth's Center

★ Science fiction stories are fictional or make-believe tales. They have imaginary characters, places, or events. They sometimes start out seeming real, but they usually include events that could never really happen. Write a science fiction story about a journey to the center of the Earth. Here are some points to get you started:
• Create a main character with an interesting personality.
• Think of an out-of the-ordinary problem for your story.
• Have the characters interact with dialogue or talking.
• Come up with a science- or technology-related solution to the problem.
Use the following story chart to help you organize your ideas.

Journey to the Center of the Earth

MAIN CHARACTER (name, personality traits)

_____

_____

SETTING What does it look like, feel like, smell like, and sound like inside the Earth?

_____

_____

BEGINNING What year is it? Who are the other main characters? What is the problem?

_____

_____

_____

MIDDLE How do the characters interact? What kind of adventure do they go on? Is there a failed attempt at solving the problem?

_____

_____

_____

END Do the characters solve the problem (happy ending) or is there a disaster (unhappy ending)?

_____

_____

_____

                          Advantage Reading Grade 5 © 2004 Creative Teaching Press

Earth's Center

Writing: Science Fiction

⭐ Write your story. Then read your story to a friend. Ask the friend to give you feedback based on these questions:
- Was the story clear or confusing?
- Did the story include extra information that will bore readers? Or did it keep you engaged and interested?
- Was the ending predictable or were you surprised?

Edit your story based on the feedback your friend gave you. Rewrite it and draw a picture to go with it on a separate piece of paper.

_____

_____

_____

_____

_____

_____

_____

_____

_____

_____

_____

_____

_____

_____

Word Practice

Predict whether you can find more V/CV or VC/V words. Create a list of words from everyday life. Read each word and see if it belongs in the V/CV or VC/V category. Divide the words using the long vowel rule (V/CV) and short vowel rule (VC/V). See which list is longer.

Fluency Practice

Make up and write down your own rap song. Practice reading it several times and then perform it for your friends. Have them keep the beat by clapping their hands or tapping their feet. Dress up for the part.

Earth Model

Make a three-dimensional model of the Earth and its interior. Use a large Styrofoam ball or make it out of paper maché. Cut the ball in half and paint and label each section. Prop up the model using a stick and a wooden or cardboard base. Include an informational poster that tells about each of the labeled parts.

Check out these books.

The Changing Earth by Rebecca Olien
    (Bridgestone Books)
Earthshake: Poems from the Ground Up by Lisa
    Westberg Peters (Greenwillow Books)
Geology: Science Activities by Graham Peacock
    (Thomson Learning)
Magic School Bus: Inside the Earth by Joanna Cole
    (Scholastic)
What's Inside Earth by Jane Kelly Kosek
    (Powerkids Press)

Name _____

Music Store

Comprehension: Prior Knowledge

Most towns and cities have music stores. They carry musical products such as CDs, tapes, and records. These come in different styles of music. List the styles of music that you know about or have heard. Write them in the label boxes on the music store CD racks below.

Structural Analysis: Root Words with the VC pattern

Music Store

★ A *root word* is a short word or word part that can be turned into another word by adding a prefix or suffix. The root words below have the VC pattern. They end with a vowel-consonant.

Vowel-**C**onsonant
rip
jet
stem

Sort through the following words to find 10 root words that have the VC pattern. Copy them on the lines.

join	beg	feel	brisk
zip	end	dab	stub
soft	tan	some	cram
map	swim	lick	pin

1. _____

2. _____

3. _____

4. _____

5. _____

6. _____

7. _____

8. _____

9. _____

10. _____

Advantage Reading Grade 5 © 2004 Creative Teaching Press

Name _____

Structural Analysis: **Suffixes**

Music Store

⭐ A *suffix* is a word ending. Add a suffix to the root word to make a new word that can be used correctly in the sentence. Write the new word on the line to complete the sentence.

-tion	-y	-ness	-ent
-ed	-ful	-able	-less
-ish	-hood	-ly	-ing
-some	-er	-est	-sion

1 elect

Jeremy asked his mom who she would vote for in the upcoming _____.

2 neighbor

Jessica liked living in her _____ because she could walk to most of her friends' houses.

3 kind

His _____ toward his classmate, Debby, was repaid when she invited him to her birthday party.

4 fish

One of my favorite springtime hobbies is to go _____ in the lake.

5 hand

The princess kissed the frog and he turned into a _____ prince.

Structural Analysis: VC/V Spelling Rule

Music Store

⭐ When adding a suffix that *begins* with a vowel to a root word that *ends* in a vowel and consonant, double the final consonant of the root word.

Add a double consonant and a suffix to each root word to make a new word. The first one is done as an example.

	Root Word **VC**		**V**	New Word
1	run	_n_	-ing	*running*
2	jog	_____	-er	_____
3	thin	_____	-est	_____
4	drop	_____	-ing	_____
5	slip	_____	-ed	_____
6	sun	_____	-y	_____
7	spin	_____	-ing	_____
8	mad	_____	-est	_____
9	red	_____	-ish	_____
10	sad	_____	-er	_____
11	fun	_____	-y	_____
12	beg	_____	-ed	_____
13	flat	_____	-est	_____

Structural Analysis: Word Building

Music Store

Combine the *root words* and *suffixes.* Be sure to add a double consonant to the words that follow the VC/V spelling rule.

1 nab + ed = _____ **6** paint + ing = _____

2 rust + y = _____ **7** sin + er = _____

3 stop + ing = _____ **8** tilt + ed = _____

4 slug + ish = _____ **9** sad + ness = _____

5 lone + ly = _____ **10** big + est = _____

Read the sentences below. Complete each sentence by adding the correct suffix from the box. Be sure to double the consonant if the word follows the VC/V spelling rule.

ly	ish	ing	er
y	ed	est	ful

11 Susan glad_____ wrap_____ the wed_____ gift.

12 Frank drop_____ the glass when the cat jump_____ .

13 The fur_____ animal went swim_____ in the pond.

14 Josh looked for a romantic table under the dim_____ lights.

15 The Scot_____ doctor looked at her pain_____ leg.

16 The Big Dip_____ is the bright_____ star tonight.

Fluency: Reading with Expression

Music Store

⭐ Read the following advertising jingle for a music store. Practice singing it to the tune of "She'll be Coming Around the Mountain." Pretend that it is your job to sing jingles for radio advertisements. Sing the jingle three times. Remember these points in order to better promote the music store that has hired you to sing:

• Sound convincing and happy.
• Sing loudly and clearly.
• Emphasize words in *italics*.

Record the jingle using a tape recorder. Play it back. Practice more and re-record to improve the quality.

Turn It Up is the music store for you.
Come on down!
Turn It Up is the music store for you.
Come on down!
We have new and used CDs.
It's *you* we aim to please.
Turn It Up is the music store for you.

Turn It Up has prices that are hard to beat.
Come on down!
Turn It Up has prices that are hard to beat.
Come on down!
If you find a better deal,
We'll match it, what a *steal!*
Turn It Up has prices that are hard to beat.

Turn It Up has lots of music to choose from.
Come on down!
Turn It Up has lots of music to choose from.
Come on down!
From rock, folk, pop, and blues,
To new age, country, it's true!
Turn It Up has lots of music to choose from.
COME ON DOWN!

Reading: Comprehension

Readers often make inferences about what they read. When an author implies or hints at meaning, but doesn't directly say something, readers can infer or reason out the meaning. Choose the best answer by making inferences about the jingle on the previous page.

1 The author of the jingle wants to

    Ⓐ buy CDs.

    Ⓑ bring down the price of CDs.

    Ⓒ get people to go to a music store.

    Ⓓ get a job working in a music store.

2 "If you find a better deal, we'll match it, what a *steal!*" means

    Ⓕ You'll get arrested if you steal CDs.

    Ⓖ Records are less expensive than CDs.

    Ⓗ Other music stores may have better deals.

    Ⓙ The store will offer prices as low as other stores.

An analogy is a type of word problem that often appears on standardized tests. It is made up of two word pairs, like this: *CD is to music store as chair is to _____.* Sometimes you will see analogy test questions written like this, with a double colon representing "as" and a single colon representing "is to."

CD : MUSIC STORE :: chair : furniture store

Solve these analogies:

3 YELLOW : LEMONS :: _____ : cherries

4 PUPPY : DOG :: kitten : _____

5 SOCK : FOOT :: mitten : _____

6 FOUR : RECTANGLE :: _____ : triangle

7 DAUGHTER : MOM :: son : _____

Name _____

Music Store

Vocabulary: Frequently Misused Words

 Sometimes a verb can be confused with a similar sounding verb. However, they cannot be used in the same way. The verb *raise* must have a direct object to complete the action. The verb *rise* is not followed by a direct object. Study the charts below to better understand the differences between *raise* and *rise*.

RAISE

Definition: to build, nurture, or lift up

Rule: *usually* followed by a direct object

Present Tense: Tom likes to <u>raise</u> chickens on the farm.

Past Tense: They <u>raised</u> the barn in one day.

Past Participle: She <u>has raised</u> three children on her own.

RISE

Definition: to get up or become elevated

Rule: *never* followed by a direct object

Present Tense: I <u>rise</u> out of bed at 7:00 a.m. every morning.

Past Tense: He <u>rose</u> to an important position at work.

Past Participle: The sun <u>has risen</u> over the mountain.

Write the correct word on the line to complete each sentence.

1 I hope to _____ a lot of money for the charity.
(raise, rise)

2 The student _____ a very good question.
(rose, raised)

3 The price of gas _____ to over two dollars.
(has raised, has risen)

4 The clouds _____ over the horizon.
(raised, rose)

5 The sun _____ in the east.
(rises, raises)

6 The man _____ the question to the council for two weeks now.
(has risen, has raised)

Vocabulary: Content Words

Music Store

Here are some common musical words. Memorize their definitions.

beat	a unit of musical rhythm
compose	to make up or create a musical piece
conductor	the leader of an orchestra
harmony	the combination of notes that is usually played or sung with a melody
instrument	a tool or device used to make music
lyrics	the words of a song
melody	the combination of notes that is usually the leading part of a song
note	a written character that represents a musical tone
opera	a dramatic musical in which the actors sing their parts
orchestra	a group of musicians playing together
rhythm	a pattern of equal or alternating beats
symphony	an orchestral or musical composition that has many instrumental parts
tempo	the rate of speed that a musical composition is played

Unscramble these words to make some of the musical words above.

1 metop   _____

2 lisryc   _____

3 chosrater   _____

4 tone   _____

5 donuccrot   _____

6 pearo   _____

7 lymedo   _____

8 teba   _____

9 mopseco   _____

10 nistumernt _____

Here is a fictional story about a middle school student who learns a valuable lesson about choosing the right friends. Read the story and then answer the questions on page 59.

A Lesson on Friendship

So far, Trevor Chavez liked going to the middle school. The cafeteria had a salad bar and soda machines. The elementary school didn't have those things. It also didn't have lockers. At the middle school, everyone had their own locker to store their books and personal belongings. They could even decorate the inside with stickers and photos. Trevor had his locker decorated by the first week of school. He used pictures that he cut out from his old skateboard magazines.

The other good thing about the middle school was all the new people that Trevor was meeting. He met a friendly girl, Shelby, in his science class. Shelby usually sat next to Trevor and giggled every time Mr. Drummond talked about frog guts. Then there were the players on his soccer team. The team captains, Mike and Josh, had a nickname for Trevor, "the secret weapon." Trevor figured it was because he was short, but fast on the field. He always managed to score at least twice during practice games.

One group of boys that Trevor hoped to meet carried their skateboards out to the parking lot every day after school. "They must have a skate ramp set up somewhere," Trevor thought to himself as he passed them on his walk home. He wondered where it was and how big it was.

Trevor decided to skate to school. Maybe that way he could meet up with the boys on his way home. Trevor was surprised when one of them stopped to talk to him in the hallway that same day. Trevor was putting his skateboard in his locker and pulling out some books for his first class.

"Hey, cool skate pictures," the boy said as he peered into Trevor's locker.

Advantage Reading Grade 5 © 2004 Creative Teaching Press

"Thanks. They're from *Skate Easy*. I got a subscription for my birthday last year. Do you know that magazine?" Trevor asked. He then realized that the boy must have seen it before. For a moment he wished he hadn't asked such a silly question.

"I see you brought your board to school. My name's Ray."

"I'm Trevor." The boys shook hands.

"The guys and I are going to practice some tricks after school today. Want to come along?"

"Sure," replied Trevor eagerly. Then the first bell rang. Ray hurried down the hallway.

"We always meet at the front door after the last class," he shouted back to Trevor. Trevor quickly scooped up his books and dashed off to science class. He hoped the seat next to Shelby was still free.

When school was over, Trevor found Ray and two friends sitting on a bench outside the front door. They were joking around when Trevor approached them. "Hi, Ray," he said.

Ray responded, "Hi, Trev. Can I call you Trev? This is Jeff and Tom. We're going to Tom's house. His dad built him a loop ramp."

"Sounds like fun. Which way?" asked Trevor.

"We take a shortcut through the woods over there." Ray pointed to a dense thicket of bushes and trees behind the school. The boys started walking in that direction. About a half mile into the walk, the group stopped. Ray reached into his shoulder bag and pulled out a pack of cigarettes. The boys each took out a cigarette and began to light up. "Want a smoke?" he asked Trevor, offering him the pack.

"No thanks," replied Trevor. It was the first time he had been offered a cigarette. Although he felt good about the answer that he had practiced in his head many times before, Trevor couldn't help but feel a little left out. After all, the others were smoking together and they seemed to be having fun.

After a few minutes, the boys put out their cigarettes and continued walking. When they reached the street again, Trevor could see a large wooden loop ramp in a driveway. He opened his mouth in surprise and said, "Wow! That looks awesome!"

Ray took out his board first and flew down the ramp. He spun into the loop and fell on the way down. The boys all laughed and cheered. They took out their boards and each had a turn on the ramp.

Trevor was having a great time. Jeff even showed him a new trick: how to get the board into your hands without having to bend down to pick it up.

After a couple of hours, Trevor told the boys, "I've got to go. My dad wants me to help mow the lawn today. Thanks for having me along."

Ray said, "No problem. Want to hang out on Saturday? We're going to that new music store in town."

"Sure. Sounds like fun."

"We're meeting at Jeff's house at noon," Ray told him.

"See you then," Trevor said as he tried out his new trick. He stepped down hard on the edge of his board. It popped up and he reached out to grab it.

At soccer practice the next day, Mike said to Trevor, "We missed you at practice yesterday." Josh spoke next, "Yeah, we need to get our secret weapon ready for the game on Saturday."

"Don't worry," Trevor said. "I'm going to be in top form at Saturday's game." Trevor suddenly remembered that he promised to go to the music store at noon. He hoped that the skate pack wouldn't spend all day there. He needed to be at the school field by 1:45 in the afternoon in order to warm up for the game.

On Saturday, Trevor ate a full breakfast. He wanted to have plenty of energy for the game later that day. He found a large backpack and stuffed his cleats and team uniform into it. He planned on changing into his uniform just before the game. Trevor made a sandwich and put it in his bag. It was almost noon. He told his dad where he was going and headed out the door.

The skate pack was sitting on Jeff's front porch when Trevor walked up to greet them. "Hi, guys," he said.

"What's in the bag?" asked Jeff.

"I've got my soccer stuff with me. After we check out the music store, I'm going to my game at school. Do you want to come?"

"Maybe some other time," Ray said. "Let's get going. I want to see if the store has the new Raging Bull CD."

Advantage Reading Grade 5 © 2004 Creative Teaching Press

The group walked to the bus stop where they caught a bus to town. The sidewalks were crowded because of the warm spring weather. The boys pushed their way through people until they reached the music store. Trevor followed them.

Once inside, everyone went in a different direction. Jeff went to watch music videos playing on a large screen. Tom was listening to music at a table that had a CD player and headphones. Ray went to a rack to look at the CDs. Trevor went right to the R section and found the Raging Bull CD.

Trevor showed the CD to Ray. "I found it first," he teased. Trevor waved it in front of Ray's face, taunting him.

"Hey, give me that," Ray said as he grabbed the disk out of Trevor's hand. He studied it closely and then said, "Turn around."

"Why?" asked Trevor.

"Just do it," demanded Ray.

Trevor shrugged his shoulders and turned around. Then he felt a tug on his backpack and he heard it unzipping. He took off the pack and saw the CD hanging out of the opening. "What are you doing? Are you going to steal it?" he asked Ray with a puzzled look on his face.

"No, _you_ are," whispered Ray. "In order to be in our club, you have to steal something. We all did it. Now it's your turn," Ray explained quietly, looking around to make sure no one was watching.

Predict the outcome. What will happen next in the story? What do you think Trevor will do?
Write your predictions on the lines.

_____

_____

_____

Trevor thought it over a minute as Ray continued to put the CD into the backpack. "Should I just do it?" he wondered. "Will I get caught? Is this what I have to do to be friends with these guys?" Trevor felt his stomach start to get tight. His head started to throb. The whole thing didn't feel right to him.

"I'm not stealing it," Trevor said boldly.

"Shhh," Ray held his finger to his mouth. "Someone might hear us."

"I don't care," Trevor went on, "because I'm not going to walk out of here with that CD in my bag. If you want it so badly, *you* take it."

"Fine, I will," Ray said matter-of-factly.

Trevor turned around and walked toward the exit door. He didn't want to stick around in case Ray got caught. Besides, he had a game to get to.

As he left the store, Trevor looked down at his watch. "Oh no!" he shouted. His watch showed 1:25 p.m. He had five minutes to get to the bus stop to catch the bus back to school. The next bus wasn't leaving until 2:00 and that's when the game would start. He ran as fast as his legs would carry him.

Trevor jumped onto the bus just as the doors were closing. He sat down and leaned against the back of the seat. He was panting like a dog. His face was red hot and his hair was stuck to his forehead.

By the time the bus got to his stop, Trevor was still breathing pretty hard. He jumped off the bus and saw Mike and Josh straight ahead. They were already in their uniforms. Trevor walked over to them.

"Glad you could make it!" Josh said to him.

"We were expecting you to ride up on your skateboard," Mike said jokingly.

"No, I'm through with that for a while," Trevor told them. "And don't worry, the secret weapon is already warmed up."

Reading: Comprehension

After reading *A Lesson on Friendship* on pages 54 through 58, answer questions 1 through 5.

1 What is the story mainly about?

_____

_____

2 Why was Trevor nicknamed "the secret weapon" by his teammates?

Ⓕ He liked to skate.   Ⓗ He was the worst player.

Ⓖ He always scored goals.   Ⓙ He liked danger.

3 Why is the story called *A Lesson on Friendship*? What lesson do you think Trevor learned about friendship?

_____

_____

4 Why did Trevor become friends with the boys in the "skate pack"?

Ⓕ He wanted friends to skate with.

Ⓖ He wanted friends to smoke with.

Ⓗ He wanted to learn about music.

Ⓙ He wanted to learn how to steal.

5 Which statement do you think Ray would most likely agree with?

Ⓐ Smoking is bad for your health.

Ⓑ Skateboarding is a dangerous and scary sport.

Ⓒ Friends should not ask other friends to steal for them.

Ⓓ Friends should do whatever is asked of them, no matter what it is.

Analyzing Characters
Stories usually have characters. A written work shows what its characters are like through their feelings and actions.

Reports contain news and information. They are found in newspapers, magazines, and other publications. Read the following report about downloading music from the Internet. Then answer the questions on page 61.

Decrease in Music Sales Due to Free Downloads

In 2001, America saw a four percent decrease in music sales. Who is to blame for the slump? According to recording companies, it's consumers with computers. High-speed Internet connections allow people to download music easily. Anyone with a fast computer can get a free copy of their favorite new song.

The issue of free music has recently been taken to court. The record companies won most of their battles. The courts ruled that the music is protected by copyright laws. Newer Internet companies have come up with a clever solution. They offer a "pay by the song" option. On their sites, people can download single songs for a small fee. Part of that fee goes to the recording companies. For singers and musicians, this means getting their fair share too.

But can music stores survive the threat to their sales? Now people don't have to go to a store to buy the latest CD in order to hear their favorite song. They can download it from the Internet. Some music stores are responding with lower prices and more advertising. They hope that loyal customers will keep returning.

And what about the singers and musicians? What do they think about selling music on the Internet? Most singers are happy with the free advertising. They want people to listen to their music and tell their friends about it. Other musicians would rather have people buy entire albums instead of single songs. They say that's the way their less popular songs get heard and appreciated.

Only one thing is for sure. Music fans will always buy music. How they get it will keep changing. For businesses that are looking toward the future, that means changing with the times.

Advantage Reading Grade 5 © 2004 Creative Teaching Press

Reading: **Comprehension**

Fill in the bubble next to the correct answer.

1 What is the article mainly about?

Ⓐ creativity in music writing

Ⓑ copyright laws in the music industry

Ⓒ the latest free download sites on the Internet

Ⓓ how downloading music is affecting the music industry

2 What are two opinions held by singers and musicians about downloading music?

_____

_____

_____

_____

3 According to the article, what is the cause of the decrease in music sales?

Ⓐ Music stores have increased their prices.

Ⓑ People don't want tapes and records anymore.

Ⓒ People have less money to spend on music, toys, and games

Ⓓ People are downloading music from the Internet instead of buying it in stores.

4 What effect did the decrease in music sales have on music stores?

Ⓕ Music stores made less money and lost business.

Ⓖ Music stores closed down and went out of business.

Ⓗ Music stores were not affected by the decrease in sales.

Ⓙ Music stores started providing Internet service to customers.

Cause and Effect
Events in stories and a character's changed feelings have to do with cause and effect relationships. Things happen for a reason. The effect is what happened and the cause is why it happened.

Music Store

Graphic Information: **Sequence Chains**

⭐ Sequence chains organize information in a specific order. They can be used to show the order of events that happened or the order of steps to take.

The sequence chain below shows the order of events that led up to Tommy Storm's big success as a singer. Study the sequence chain and then answer the questions on page 63.

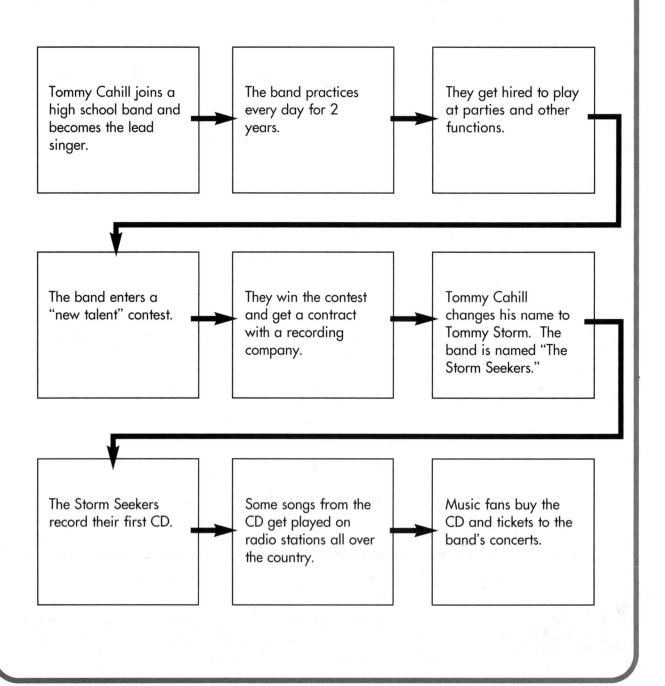

Tommy Cahill joins a high school band and becomes the lead singer. → The band practices every day for 2 years. → They get hired to play at parties and other functions.

The band enters a "new talent" contest. → They win the contest and get a contract with a recording company. → Tommy Cahill changes his name to Tommy Storm. The band is named "The Storm Seekers."

The Storm Seekers record their first CD. → Some songs from the CD get played on radio stations all over the country. → Music fans buy the CD and tickets to the band's concerts.

   Advantage Reading Grade 5 © 2004 Creative Teaching Press

Reading: Comprehension

Fill in the bubble next to the correct anwer.

1 What happened before the band won the "new talent" contest?
- Ⓐ Tommy changed his name.
- Ⓑ Radio stations played the band's songs.
- Ⓒ The band practiced and played at parties.
- Ⓓ The band got a recording contract to make a CD.

2 What happened after the band got a recording contract?
- Ⓕ Tommy became the lead singer.
- Ⓖ The band was named "The Storm Seekers."
- Ⓗ The band rehearsed their songs for 2 years.
- Ⓙ The band played at parties and other functions.

3 What is the most likely reason Tommy changed his name?
- Ⓐ Tommy didn't like his last name.
- Ⓑ Tommy got struck by lightning during a storm.
- Ⓒ People confused Tommy for someone else with the same last name.
- Ⓓ Tommy thought that an exciting last name would give him a better chance to become famous.

4 Think of another way that Tommy could have met his goal of becoming a famous singer. Write your ideas on the lines below.

_____

_____

_____

_____

_____

Name _____

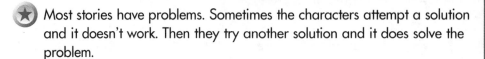

Music Store

⭐ Most stories have problems. Sometimes the characters attempt a solution and it doesn't work. Then they try another solution and it does solve the problem.

Write a story about a record store. The problem is that the record store is losing business. They are not selling as many music products as they used to. Create a character who helps the store solve their problem. Use the Problem/Solution Story Planner form below to help organize your ideas.

These questions can be used as a guide:
• Who has the problem?
• What is the problem?
• Where is the problem?
• Why is there a problem? Why are sales down?
• What attempts were made to solve the problem?
• Did those attempts work? What were the results? What happened?
• What were the end results? How was the problem finally solved?

Problem/Solution Story Planner

Who _____

What _____

When _____

Where _____

Why _____

⬇

Attemped Solutions   **Results**

1 _____ ⟶ 1 _____

2 _____ ⟶ 2 _____

⬇

End Results

_____

_____

Writing: **Fiction**

_____

_____

_____

_____

_____

_____

_____

_____

_____

_____

_____

_____

_____

_____

Read your story to an adult you know who works in or has worked in a business. Ask this person to give you feedback. Ask these questions about your story:
• Were the solutions interesting?
• Was the final solution one that really would have helped the store?
• What are some other solutions that could have solved the problem?

Make changes to your story solutions based on the feedback you got.

Word Practice

Keep a notepad and a pencil next to your favorite book. As you read a page, jot down all the words that have a double consonant and follow the VC/V spelling rule.

Speech Practice

Write a skit. Create parts for several characters. Think of a problem and come up with a solution that gives the story a funny ending. Write a script for your skit.

Fluency Practice

Invite your friends to read the skit you wrote. Choose parts and practice reading the lines. When you are ready, perform your skit at school.

Art Activity

Pretend you are a member of a band. Come up with a band name. Think of titles for the songs on your first CD. Design CD artwork that represents you and the band. Draw your cover and label for the back of the CD with your song titles. Slip it into a CD case and show it to a friend or teacher.

Check out these books.

The Kingfisher Young People's Book of Music by
    Clive Wilson (Larousse Kingfisher Chambers)
Learn Songwriting by Caroline Hooper
    (Usborne Publishing Ltd.)
Lives of the Musician by Kathleen Krull (Harcourt)
Story of the Orchestra by Meredith Hamilton
    (Black Dog & Leventhal)
Usborne Story of Music by Eileen O'Brien
    (EDC Publications)

Science Museum

Comprehension: Prior Knowledge

There is a lot to see and learn about in a science museum. Some museums have dinosaur exhibits. Some have displays on the human body. Many have planetariums where you can see projected images of the stars and planets. What is your favorite exhibit or display at the science museum? Describe it on the lines and then draw a picture of it in the box below.

_____

_____

_____

_____

_____

_____

_____

Structural Analysis: **The Consonant -*le* Syllable**

Science Museum

⭐ A consonant -*le* syllable (**C-le**) is a final syllable. The *e* is silent and the syllable sounds like /ê l/.

Read these sentences and listen to how the final **C-le** syllables in the **bold** words all sound the same:

• The children all stood in a **circle** to play the game.
• **Purple** is her favorite color.
• We saw a **turtle** crossing the road.

Choose from the consonant -*le* syllables in the box below to add to each of the following syllables to make a word. Then write the whole word and say it. The first one is done as an example.

kle	fle	tle	ble	dle

1 cra _dle_ _cradle_

2 ta _____ _____

3 bat _____ _____

4 ri _____ _____

5 spar _____ _____

6 mar _____ _____

7 set _____ _____

8 ruf _____ _____

9 hud _____ _____

10 buc _____ _____

11 rat _____ _____

12 han _____ _____

13 fa _____ _____

14 sta _____ _____

15 cat _____ _____

16 pad _____ _____

17 tac _____ _____

18 gen _____ _____

19 star _____ _____

20 ca _____ _____

 Advantage Reading Grade 5 © 2004 Creative Teaching Press

Name _____

Science Museum

⭐ When a word ends in a consonant -le syllable, divide the word just *before* the first consonant before the *le*. Divide these words into syllables using the **C-le** rule. Then write their syllable parts on the lines below. The first one is done as an example.

1. bugle   _____bu_____ / _____gle_____

2. idle   _____ / _____

3. stumble   _____ / _____

4. brittle   _____ / _____

5. twinkle   _____ / _____

6. poodle   _____ / _____

7. maple   _____ / _____

8. circle   _____ / _____

9. ankle   _____ / _____

10. noble   _____ / _____

11. raffle   _____ / _____

12. gurgle   _____ / _____

13. bridle   _____ / _____

14. uncle   _____ / _____

15. puzzle   _____ / _____

Structural Analysis: Dividing Words with -le

Science Museum

Each of the following sentences has two consonant -le words. Circle them all.

1 I watched the stars twinkle as I settled down to sleep.

2 Kevin stumbled on a rock and hurt his ankle.

3 Please be gentle when you hold the poodle.

4 Look at that eagle flying over the maple tree.

5 The baby gurgled after drinking from the bottle.

6 Take the saddle back to the horse stable.

7 The purple glitter sparkled on the paper.

8 Sally put the flowers in the middle of the table.

Write the circled words on the lines under the categories below.

9 Words with **ble**

_____ _____ _____

10 Words with **ple**

_____ _____

11 Words with **tle**

_____ _____ _____

12 Words with **gle**

_____ _____

13 Words with **kle**

_____ _____ _____

14 Words with **dle**

_____ _____ _____

Advantage Reading Grade 5 © 2004 Creative Teaching Press

Name _____

Science Museum

Combine a final syllable from the box with the first syllable to make a two-syllable word. Write the two-syllable word on the line. The first one is done as an example.

dle	kle	fle	tle	gle

1. ea _eagle_
2. buc _____
3. ruf _____
4. can _____
5. ket _____

fle	kle	ble	cle	dle

6. tic _____
7. trem _____
8. raf _____
9. bun _____
10. mus _____

zle	tle	dle	ple	kle	ble

11. no _____
12. hud _____
13. cas _____
14. puz _____
15. tem _____

dle	tle	ble	cle	fle

16. hum _____
17. cra _____
18. rat _____
19. un _____
20. baf _____

Unscramble these three-syllable words and write them on the lines.

21. cle sta ob _____
22. ple ex am _____
23. i cle ci _____

24. par cle ti _____
25. cle mir a _____
26. cle na bar _____

Science Museum

Fluency: Reading with Phrasing

 Fluent readers put words together in short phrases. Practice reading the animal poem below three times. Here are some points to remember as you read:
- Read in natural phrases.
- Clap your hands or tap your foot as you read and stick to the beat.
- If you see a comma (,) or semicolon (;), read all the words before it in one breath.

SIMILE SAFARI

I went on an animal safari today.
Right after lunch,
my mom showed me the way.

Out of the house,
a ride on the train;
and there I was,
in the Serengeti Plains!

A cheetah, I saw first,
bolting straight through the grass,
as swift as a wind storm,
moving strong, flying fast.

He was chasing his prey,
a zebra it seemed,
a black and white swirl,
like a wet magazine.

Behind bushes and trees,
a giraffe we then saw,
rising high like a fortress,
chewing leaves with its jaws.

And off in the distance,
like an army, came marching,
a herd of wild elephants;
their trunks high and arching.

An eyeball, no, two!
Peering just above water,
a hippo was swimming,
trying not to get hotter.

And how, you ask now,
did I arrive in just minutes?
Am I in East Africa,
or at a museum exhibit?

Name _____

Reading: **Comprehension**

Use the information from the poem "Simile Safari" on page 72 to answer questions 1 through 6.

1 Where is the speaker in the poem?

    Ⓐ in a zoo

    Ⓑ in a museum

    Ⓒ on a playground

    Ⓓ on a safari in Africa

2 Who is most likely to be the speaker?

    Ⓕ a child

    Ⓖ a mother

    Ⓗ a cheetah

    Ⓙ a safari guide

3 In the poem, what is a cheetah compared to?

_____

4 In the poem, what is a zebra compared to?

_____

5 In the poem, what is a giraffe compared to?

_____

6 In the poem, what is a herd of elephants compared to?

_____

Know the Skill 👉

Similes

A *simile* is a comparison of two unlike things using *like* or *as*. Similes are often used in poetry. Here's an example: *A good book is like a good meal.* This simile suggests that a book can be as mentally nourishing and satisfying as a meal. Here's another example: *The steak was as tough as leather.* This simile suggests that a steak was as hard to chew as a piece of leather would be.

Vocabulary: **Frequently Misused Words**

Science Museum

★ Spelling mistakes that involve sound-alike words (homophones) can change the meaning of the sentence in which they are used. This creates confusion for the reader. Two frequently misused homophones are *accept* and *except*.

Write the correct word on the line to complete each sentence.

ACCEPT	**EXCEPT**
(Verb) meaning "to receive"	(Preposition) meaning "but" or "leaving out"
He <u>accepted</u> the gift. (He received it.)	Everyone volunteered to help <u>except</u> Karla.

1 The whole class went on the field trip _____ Tim.
(accept, except)

2 I won't _____ any money for the work.
(accept, except)

3 My mother did not _____ the job.
(accept, except)

4 All the kids played tennis _____ Toshi.
(accept, except)

5 Please _____ our invitation to dinner.
(accept, except)

6 It will cure all itches _____ poison ivy.
(accept, except)

7 Write a sentence using the word *accept* correctly.

_____

8 Write a sentence using the word *except* correctly.

_____

Advantage Reading Grade 5 © 2004 Creative Teaching Press

Vocabulary: **Content Words**

Science Museum

The people who put together displays and exhibits at science museums have studied in a particular field of science. For example, an ocean life exhibit is designed with the help of someone who has studied oceanography. Oceanography is the study of the ocean and its plants and animals.

The root word **logy** means to study. Add the following list of root words to the beginning of the root word **logy** to create a new word. Then define it. Each one is a scientific field of study.

Root Word   New Word

1   anthrop (means man)   +   ology   =   _____

The study of _____

2   bio (means life)   +   logy   =   _____

The study of _____

3   geo (means earth)   +   logy   =   _____

The study of _____

4   neur (means nerve)   +   ology   =   _____

The study of _____

5   zo (means animal)   +   ology   =   _____

The study of _____

6   entom (means insect)   +   ology   =   _____

The study of _____

Build a Working Volcano

Ingredients and Supplies

6 cups flour

2 cups salt

4 tablespoons cooking oil

2 cups water

plastic soda bottle

baking pan

6 drops red food coloring

6 drops liquid detergent

2 tablespoons baking soda

vinegar

Directions

1 Make some "salt dough." To do this, mix 6 cups flour, 2 cups salt, 4 tablespoons cooking oil, and 2 cups water in a large bowl. Knead and mix the ingredients with your hands until you have a firm and smooth dough ball. Add more water if necessary.

2 Stand the soda bottle upright in the baking pan. Mold the salt dough around the bottle so that it is propped up. Use the dough to build a realistic volcano using your imagination and creativity. Be careful not to cover up the bottle opening or drop any dough into the bottle.

3 Fill the bottle almost all the way with warm water and add 6 drops of red food coloring.

4 Add 6 drops of liquid detergent to the bottle.

5 Add 2 tablespoons of baking soda.

6 Slowly pour vinegar into the bottle.

7 Stand back and watch.

Reading: **Comprehension**

Fill in the bubble next to the correct answer.

1 All of the following are ingredients for "salt dough" EXCEPT _____.

    Ⓐ salt

    Ⓑ flour

    Ⓒ cooking oil

    Ⓓ baking soda

2 Which of the following directions should be done first?

    Ⓕ Use salt dough to build a realistic volcano.

    Ⓖ Add 2 tablespoons of baking soda.

    Ⓗ Slowly pour vinegar into the bottle.

    Ⓙ Fill the bottle almost all the way with warm water.

3 Which of the following is not part of the directions?

    Ⓐ Make a ball out of the salt dough.

    Ⓑ Put liquid detergent into the soda bottle.

    Ⓒ Pour some green food coloring into the soda bottle.

    Ⓓ Stand the soda bottle upright in the baking pan.

4 What is the last ingredient that should be used to build a working volcano?

    Ⓕ water

    Ⓖ vinegar

    Ⓗ cooking oil

    Ⓙ baking soda

5 Write two or more sentences to predict what will happen after Step 7.

_____

_____

_____

_____

Read the chapter from a story about a pair of friends who discover a secret entrance to a medieval castle while on a field trip to the science museum. Then answer the questions on page 82.

The Secret Portal

Chapter 1

Liz was asked to share a seat with Tommy on the bus ride to the science museum. She wouldn't have minded sitting next to him if he stayed quiet and kept to himself, but that didn't happen. As soon as they sat down, Tommy turned to her and asked, "Do you know how powerful a typical school bus engine is?"

"No," replied Liz with an annoyed look on her face.

"School buses have at least 200 pounds of horsepower! Do you know what horsepower is?"

"I don't know. A bunch of horses hidden inside the motor?" Liz answered with a little smirk, hoping that would shut Tommy up.

"No, actually, it's a term invented by engineer James Watt. The story goes that Watt was working with horses lifting coal at a coal mine. He wanted a way to talk about the power available from a horse. He learned that, on average, a mine horse could lift 22,000 pounds of work in one minute. Nowadays, we use the word horsepower to talk about cars, lawn mowers, chainsaws, and even school buses!"

Tommy kept on talking. Liz tried not to listen. She looked out the window and began day-dreaming about knights and princesses. The thought of visiting the new "Middle Ages" exhibit at the science museum was something she looked forward to. She decided to endure Tommy's babbling until they got there.

When the bus finally arrived at the museum, the students were told they had two hours to explore the exhibit on their own. Liz's face lit up. The teacher went on to explain that the only rules were to stay within the exhibit walls and to stay with their partner at all times. Liz rolled her eyes and sighed. She was stuck with Tommy. "I know a lot about the Middle Ages," he declared. "I have more books on the topic than anyone I know," he assured her.

"Oh, great," she said, trying to crack a little smile so that Tommy wouldn't feel too badly about her lack of enthusiasm.

The entrance to the exhibit was a giant drawbridge suspended over a moat with real water in it. Liz and Tommy crossed the bridge and entered the exhibit. On the stone walls were window boxes with medieval artifacts and objects in them. Tommy carefully studied each one. Liz went across the room to a table decorated with miniature houses and people and a tiny castle. She read the display information posted on the table.

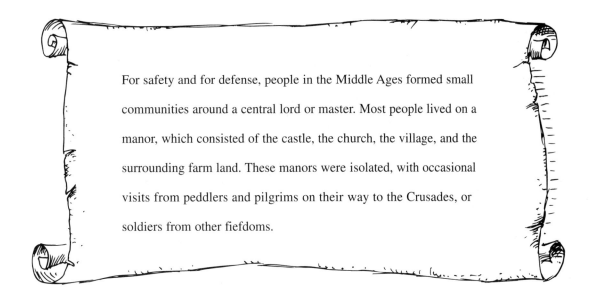

For safety and for defense, people in the Middle Ages formed small communities around a central lord or master. Most people lived on a manor, which consisted of the castle, the church, the village, and the surrounding farm land. These manors were isolated, with occasional visits from peddlers and pilgrims on their way to the Crusades, or soldiers from other fiefdoms.

Just then, Liz felt a tap on her shoulder. She jumped up, startled by the interruption. She looked back and saw Tommy's concerned face.

"We're supposed to stay together. That's what the teacher said," he warned her in a serious tone.

"Oh, calm down, Tommy. I promise I won't wander off again. Come on. Let's check out that armored knight." She grabbed Tommy's arm and he trailed behind her down a dimly lit hallway.

The frozen knight towered way above the kids. It had a chain-mail suit and was holding a long sword with one hand and a shield with the other. "Lift me up," demanded Liz.

"What?" asked Tommy.

"I said lift me up."

"Why?" he asked her.

"I want to see the knight's face," she explained. "Just interlock your hands and I'll step into them and then you lift up. Please? Let's find out what's inside of this thing."

Tommy gave in to Liz's request and hoisted her up. "Oh, I don't think I can hold you up much longer," he mumbled, clenching his teeth.

"Just another minute. I see something inside his helmet." Liz twisted her hand into an opening in the knight's helmet and yanked it out just as Tommy's hands came apart, forcing both of them to come tumbling down.

Right in front of them, a shiny object fell, making a tin-like sound as it dropped to the floor. "It's an old coin!" Liz whispered to Tommy. She picked it up and showed it to him. It had a big letter *A* engraved on both sides. "It must have been hidden inside the knight's helmet."

"Well, we better bring it with us so we can give it to a museum worker," said Tommy. "It probably belongs in one of the displays." He leaned his hand against the wall to push himself up. The stone under his hand felt cold and damp. "Wow, this exhibit is remarkably realistic," he thought to himself. Just then, the stone suddenly sank in and a small crevice in the wall began to creak open.

"Look, a secret door!" exclaimed Liz. "Tommy, you opened a secret door!" Liz jammed the coin into her pocket and crawled into the space.

"You said you wouldn't wander off!" Tommy pleaded, but it was too late. The crevice slowly started to close up. Tommy managed to squeeze himself in before it sealed shut.

On the other side was another hallway. "This is NOT part of the exhibit," Tommy said in a frustrated voice. He was pushing against every rock on the wall, trying to get the door to open again. In the distance, a faint voice was calling, "Help! Help! I'm over here! Help!"

"Well, don't just sit there," said Tommy. "Let's go and help!" he said as he got up and brushed himself off.

Liz couldn't believe her ears. "Now you're the one wandering off!" she called to him as he marched down the corridor.

 Advantage Reading Grade 5 © 2004 Creative Teaching Press

The corridor wound around to a dark room with a staircase leading up. To the side of it was a big wooden door. "I think we're in a dungeon," said Liz.

"Psst … over here," whispered a voice from behind the door. Tiny hands grabbed the iron bars across the small, square opening halfway up the door. "Help me. Please!"

"Who are you?" Tommy asked as he leaned closer to the door."

"I'm Donovan Little, one of Lord Quagmire's vassals."

"What's a vassal?" Liz asked Tommy.

Tommy whispered, "It's a person who works for the lord of a castle in exchange for land. Under the feudalism system, a vassal is required to attend to the lord at his court, help administer justice, and pay taxes."

Liz felt a brief moment of relief as Tommy spoke. At least she had Tommy by her side. He was a practical expert in medieval culture. If there was anyone to get sent back in time with, Tommy would be her first pick.

The voice from behind the door continued. "Lord Quagmire locked me up in here when I refused to do his bidding. He sent me with the tax collector to visit every house in the village. We were to collect more taxes. Those who didn't pay were to be locked up in the lord's dungeons. Many of the peasants are poor and could not pay the large sums of money. I defied the lord and was the first one locked up in the castle dungeon. And here I have been sitting and waiting for my fate. Will you help me get out?"

"How?" asked Liz.

"The key to the lock is behind you, on the wall."

Liz and Tommy turned and saw a large, iron key ring hanging high on a peg. There were at least a dozen keys dangling from it. Tommy jumped up and hit the key ring with his fist. The keys came crashing down to the floor, making a loud ringing sound that echoed throughout the hallways.

"What's all that noise down there?" a deep voice shouted from the top of the stairs.

"Hurry, unlock the door before the guard comes down," begged Donovan.

Tommy grabbed the key ring and tried turning the lock with a key. It didn't work. He tried another. That one didn't work either. The kids could hear heavy footsteps coming down the stairs.

"Hurry," pleaded Liz.

Just as the guard came into sight on the staircase, they heard "click." One of the keys worked. The lock turned and the door flew open. Out came a tiny little man with a long snow-white beard. He was wearing a purple cape and tiny purple shoes. The guard leapt into the air to try and seize him, but he suddenly turned into a cloud of smoke.

"How did you do that?" asked Liz.

"I'm Donovan the wizard, not Donovan the vassal, you silly child," responded the little man in a stern voice. His eyes glowed red. "My powers lie within those who look into my eyes. I would vanish you both, had you not rescued me from a place where my eyes could not be seen. So, instead, I will trade places with you."

Out of nowhere, a gust of wind hurled Liz and Tommy into the cell. The wooden door shut and they were locked in. Little footsteps could be heard marching up the stairs. "Now, for the gold coin. If I could only find the gold coin of Avalon … the gold coin," his voice faded into the distance.

"Now we're really stuck," said Tommy.

"Yeah, but we have the golden coin," Liz replied as she pulled the shiny coin from her pocket and smiled at Tommy.

End of Chapter 1

Reading: Comprehension

Fill in the bubble next to the correct answer.

1 What is the setting for most of the story?

Ⓐ in a castle

Ⓑ in a school bus

Ⓒ at a science fair

Ⓓ in an art museum

2 What is the most likely explanation for the secret door?

Ⓕ The museum is really a castle.

Ⓖ It is part of the museum exhibit.

Ⓗ Donovan used his magic to make it.

Ⓙ It was built by Lord Quagmire to escape from Donovan.

3 Which of these statements about Donovan is probably true?

Ⓐ Donovan isn't really a magician.

Ⓑ Donovan works for Lord Quagmire.

Ⓒ Donovan wants to help the kids get home.

Ⓓ Donovan's magic doesn't work if his eyes are covered.

4 What is the most likely title for the next chapter?

Ⓕ Lost in a Cave   Ⓗ Donovan Saves the Day

Ⓖ Back at the Museum   Ⓙ A Visit to Lord Quagmire

5 How did Liz's feelings about Tommy change toward the end of the story?
Use examples from the story in your answer.

_____

_____

_____

_____

 Advantage Reading Grade 5 © 2004 Creative Teaching Press

Graphic Information: **Maps**

Science Museum

⭐ Maps are visual representations or plans of a place. Maps help people find their way around. They show us where we are in relation to other places. Study the map of the layout of a science museum. Then answer the questions on page 84.

Floor Map of the Science and Nature Museum

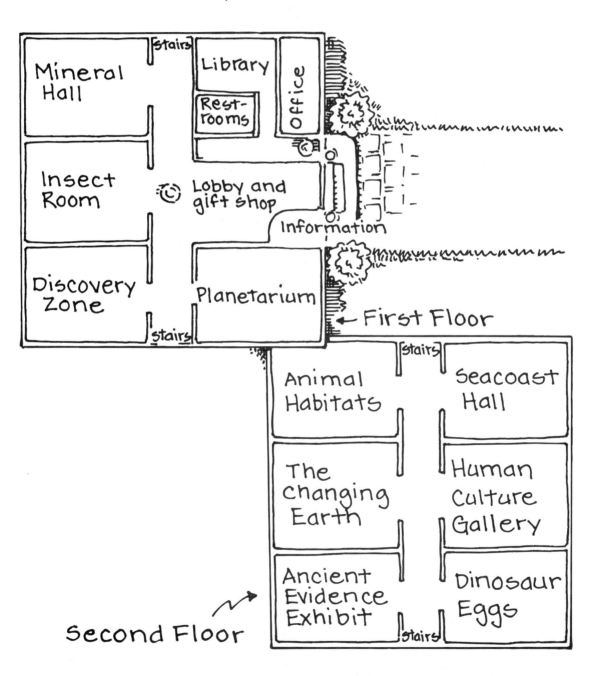

Fill in the bubble next to the correct answer.

1 In what part of the museum would you most likely learn about stars and planets?

Ⓐ Office

Ⓑ Planetarium

Ⓒ Mineral Hall

Ⓓ Insect Room

2 In what part of the museum would you most likely learn about coral reefs?

Ⓕ Seacoast Hall

Ⓖ Mineral Room

Ⓗ Discovery Zone

Ⓙ Human Culture Gallery

3 In what part of the museum would you most likely find old tools?

Ⓐ Dinosaur Eggs

Ⓑ Discovery Zone

Ⓒ The Changing Earth

Ⓓ Ancient Evidence Exhibit

4 What would most likely not be found on the second floor?

Ⓕ a lion den

Ⓖ spider eggs

Ⓗ dinosaur fossils

Ⓙ model of the ocean floor

5 In what part of the museum would you most likely learn about how and where elephants sleep?

Ⓐ Insect Room

Ⓑ Dinosaur Eggs

Ⓒ Animal Habitats

Ⓓ Human Culture Gallery

Science Museum

Writing: Technical Writing

⭐ Technical writing usually includes cause and effect relationships. For example, a medical journal article about the effects of a certain medicine might explain the following:

EFFECT (what)   The patient got better.
CAUSE (why)   The patient took the medicine.

Try the science experiment on page 76. After you have built the volcano and watched the outcome, fill out the cause and effect form below.

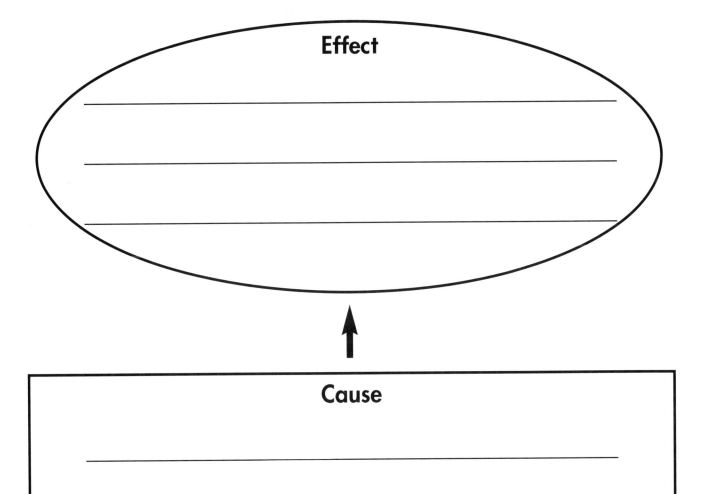

Effect

Cause

Name _____

Science Museum

Writing: Technical Writing

⭐ Write a journal article for a science magazine comparing the results of the experiment to what happens in a real volcano. To help you get started, use the information from the cause/effect graphic organizer on page 85.

Remember these important points when writing your journal article:
- Briefly describe the experiment you conducted.
- Describe the outcome and results (effect).
- Come up with a theory or reason why this happened (cause).
- Compare the process to a real volcanic eruption.

_____

_____

_____

_____

_____

_____

_____

_____

_____

_____

_____

_____

_____

_____

Word Practice

Ask a parent how many words he or she thinks you can find with the suffix *-le*. Try to beat the estimate. Look for words everywhere: in the grocery store, at the park, on street signs, on menus. Then divide the words that you find into syllables and write a sentence using each one.

Writing Practice

Do some research on the nearest science museum to your home. Find out what kinds of exhibits and displays they have. Find out the price of admission and the hours of operation. Then write a persuasive letter to a parent convincing him or her to take you to the museum. Include some reasons why the trip would be educational for you and what you hope to learn.

Fluency Practice

Read your favorite poem using a different voice for each stanza or part. Change the intonation of your voice as you read. Make your voice rise for questions. Make your voice expressive to communicate exclamation points. Practice reciting the poem several times and then record yourself using a tape recorder.

Window Box Science Exhibit

Pretend that you have been hired to design a new science exhibit at a museum. Think of a theme and design an exhibit filled with objects, artifacts, and hands-on activities. Be creative. Draw your exhibit on a sheet of paper and then make a small model of it. Use construction paper for the walls and make miniature informational posters to hang up. Then find or create small items for your model.

Check out these books.

Easy Science Experiments by Diane Molleson (Scholastic)

Experiments in Science: How Does it Work? by David Glover (DK Publishing)

Geology Science Activities by Graham Peacock (Thomson Learning)

Hands-On Science by Sarah Angliss (Houghton Mifflin)

Mrs. Brown on Exhibit: And Other Museum Poems by Susan Katz (Simon & Schuster)

Name _____

Costume Party

Comprehension: **Prior Knowledge**

Have you ever been to a costume party? What was it like? What kinds of games were played? What types of costumes did people wear? Write what you know about costume parties on the lines. In the box, draw a picture of a costume you would like to wear to a costume party.

_____

_____

_____

_____

_____

_____

_____

_____

_____

Advantage Reading Grade 5 © 2004 Creative Teaching Press

Structural Analysis: V/V Syllabication Rule

Costume Party

⭐ Some words are divided into syllables between two vowels. When a word is divided between two vowels, the first of the two vowels has a long vowel sound.

Vowel/**V**owel

cha/os   bo/a   qui/et   ne/on   cru/el

Divide the following two-syllable words using the V/V rule. Then write their syllable parts on the lines. The first one is done as an example.

1 poet   __po__ / __et__

2 truant   _____ / _____

3 diet   _____ / _____

4 fluid   _____ / _____

5 science   _____ / _____

6 react   _____ / _____

7 dual   _____ / _____

8 meow   _____ / _____

Each of the following three-syllable words already has one syllable division. Decide where to apply the V/V rule and make another syllable division. Write the syllable parts on the lines and read each word. The first one is done as an example.

9 mu/seum   __mu__ / __se__ / __um__

10 nu/cleus _____ / _____ / _____

11 oa/sis   _____ / _____ / _____

12 vio/lin   _____ / _____ / _____

13 me/teor   _____ / _____ / _____

14 chaot/ic _____ / _____ / _____

15 io/dine   _____ / _____ / _____

16 coin/cide _____ / _____ / _____

Name _____

Costume Party

⭐ The suffix -*et* has the /êt/ or /ît/ sound. Add the suffix -*et* to the following words. Then rewrite and divide each word using the V/V rule.

1 rock_____   _____   **4** du_____   _____

2 qui_____   _____   **5** po_____   _____

3 di_____   _____   **6** midg_____   _____

The suffixes -*al* and -*el* have the /êl/ or /âl/ sound. Write each word on a line under the correct category. Then divide each word using the V/V rule.

| trial   fuel   steal   dial   cruel   duel |

Words with *al* ending   **Words with *el* ending**

7 _____   **10** _____

8 _____   **11** _____

9 _____   **12** _____

The suffixes -*ant* and -*ent* have the /ênt/ or /ânt/ sound. Write each word on a line under the correct category. Then divide each word using the V/V rule.

| truant   fluent   client   giant |

Words with *ant* ending   **Words with *ent* ending**

13 _____   **15** _____

14 _____   **16** _____

                                    Advantage Reading Grade 5 © 2004 Creative Teaching Press

Name _____

Costume Party

Structural Analysis: VV and V/V Words

Some of the following words have one syllable and a double vowel (VV). Other words have two syllables and can be divided between the vowels (V/V). Read the words to decide which column they belong in. Then write them on the blank lines in the correct column. Divide the two-syllable words using the V/V rule.

jail	preach	create	poem	dial	toe
lion	pie	paint	fruit	react	spoil
poach	science	suit	ruin	neon	truant

One-Syllable Words (VV)	Two-Syllable Words (V/V)

Use some of the words above to fill in the blanks and complete the sentences.

1   My favorite _____ is an orange.

2   Pick up the phone and _____ the number.

3   Let's _____ the sign bright, _____ yellow.

4   If you spill juice on your _____, you will _____ it.

5   You might _____ your dinner if you eat _____ first.

Structural Analysis: **Word Building**

Costume Party

Match the syllables to make a two-syllable word. Then write it on the line.

1 tri   ot
      ant   _____
      umph

4 flu   id
       eon   _____
       et

2 di   et
     ate   _____
     us

5 ri   a
     ot   _____
     eum

3 cre   ine
      ate   _____
      al

6 cru   ent
       ium   _____
       el

Unscramble the following three-syllable words. Write the word on the line.

7   lence   vi   o   _____

8   me   der   an   _____

9   sis   o   a   _____

10   o   pi   neer   _____

11   ro   o   de   _____

12   us   cle   nu   _____

13   lin   vi   o   _____

14   o   dine   i   _____

15   u   et   min   _____

16   flu   in   ence   _____

Costume Party

Fluency: **Reading with Intonation**

⭐ Intonation is the rise and fall of pitch in one's voice. Intonation helps to express a range of feelings and emotions. Practice reading the telephone conversation skit below three times. Here are some points to remember as you read:

- Emphasize words in *italics*.
- Change your voice for each speaker.
- "Read" the punctuation; adjust your tone to match it.
- Make your voice rise and fall to convey feelings like sadness, joy, and anger.

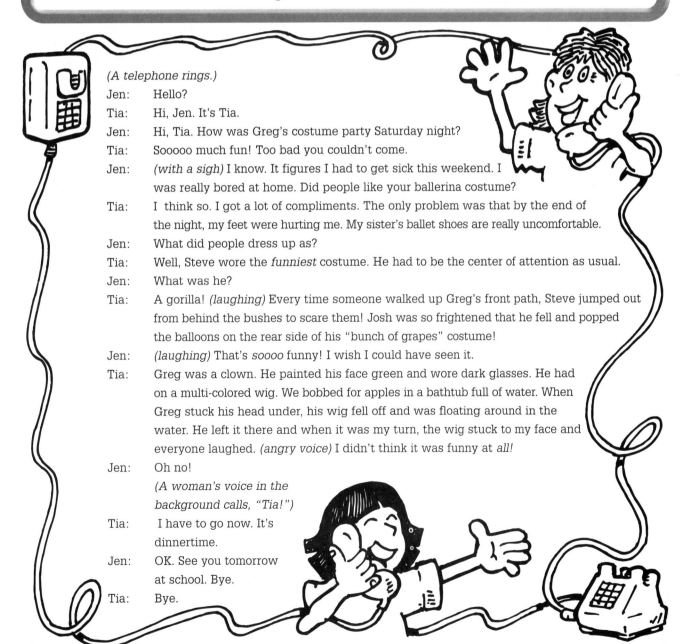

(A telephone rings.)

Jen: Hello?

Tia: Hi, Jen. It's Tia.

Jen: Hi, Tia. How was Greg's costume party Saturday night?

Tia: Sooooo much fun! Too bad you couldn't come.

Jen: *(with a sigh)* I know. It figures I had to get sick this weekend. I was really bored at home. Did people like your ballerina costume?

Tia: I think so. I got a lot of compliments. The only problem was that by the end of the night, my feet were hurting me. My sister's ballet shoes are really uncomfortable.

Jen: What did people dress up as?

Tia: Well, Steve wore the *funniest* costume. He had to be the center of attention as usual.

Jen: What was he?

Tia: A gorilla! *(laughing)* Every time someone walked up Greg's front path, Steve jumped out from behind the bushes to scare them! Josh was so frightened that he fell and popped the balloons on the rear side of his "bunch of grapes" costume!

Jen: *(laughing)* That's *soooo* funny! I wish I could have seen it.

Tia: Greg was a clown. He painted his face green and wore dark glasses. He had on a multi-colored wig. We bobbed for apples in a bathtub full of water. When Greg stuck his head under, his wig fell off and was floating around in the water. He left it there and when it was my turn, the wig stuck to my face and everyone laughed. *(angry voice)* I didn't think it was funny at *all*!

Jen: Oh no!

(A woman's voice in the background calls, "Tia!")

Tia: I have to go now. It's dinnertime.

Jen: OK. See you tomorrow at school. Bye.

Tia: Bye.

Reading: **Comprehension**

Use the information from the telephone conversation skit on page 93 to answer questions 1 through 5.

1 Where did the party take place?

- Ⓐ at a house
- Ⓑ at a school
- Ⓒ at a museum
- Ⓓ at a theme park

2 What was Tia's costume?

- Ⓕ a clown
- Ⓖ a princess
- Ⓗ a ballerina
- Ⓙ a bunch of grapes

3 Why was Tia angry?

- Ⓐ The shoes she wore hurt her feet.
- Ⓑ Jen didn't go to the party with her.
- Ⓒ The balloons on her costume popped.
- Ⓓ Everyone laughed when a wig got stuck to her face.

4 Why didn't Jen go to the party?

- Ⓕ She was too sick to go.
- Ⓖ She wasn't invited to the party.
- Ⓗ Her mother wouldn't let her go.
- Ⓙ She was away on vacation that week.

5 If there was a contest for the funniest costume, who would Tia pick as the winner?

- Ⓐ Josh
- Ⓑ Greg
- Ⓒ Steve
- Ⓓ herself

Advantage Reading Grade 5 © 2004 Creative Teaching Press

Vocabulary: Frequently Misused Words

Costume Party

The words *farther* and *further* are both used when talking about advancement. However, *farther* refers to actual distance and *further* refers to figurative distance. *Further* can also be used to mean "additional." Study the chart below to better understand the differences between *farther* and *further*.

FARTHER (Adjective) meaning "physical advancement in length or distance" Example: The airport is <u>farther</u> away than I thought it would be.
FURTHER (Adverb) meaning "physical advancement in time, degree, or amount" Example: He explained the game rules <u>further</u>. (Adjective) meaning "additional" or "to a greater extent or degree" Example: This matter requires <u>further</u> investigation.

Write the correct word on the blank line to complete each sentence.

1 How much _____ do we have to drive?
(farther, further)

2 Do you have any _____ plans for the summer?
(farther, further)

3 We walked _____ today than we did yesterday.
(farther, further)

4 Boston is _____ north than Hartford.
(farther, further)

5 How much _____ do I have to read in this book?
(farther, further)

6 Your project requires _____ research and work.
(farther, further)

7 Write a sentence using the word *farther* correctly.

_____

8 Write a sentence using the word *further* correctly.

_____

Grammar: **Adjectives and Adverbs**

Costume Party

★ *Adjectives* are words used to describe nouns, such as people, places, animals, or things. *Adverbs* describe verbs, adjectives, and other adverbs. Many adverbs end with *ly*.

Adjectives describe (nouns)   Example: I like to read in a quiet room.

Adverbs describe (verbs)   Example: He speaks slowly.

Read the sentences. Underline the adjective or adverb in each sentence and circle the noun or verb it describes.

1. She wore a colorful wig.

2. The guests quickly walked to the party.

3. She had a beautiful dress on.

4. The fur on his costume was fluffy.

5. I bravely walked into the room in my costume.

6. The skin on the mask looked wrinkled.

7. We waited patiently for the contest to begin.

8. The face on my friend's costume was scary.

9. Tim dressed as a lion and growled fiercely.

10. The person dressed as a ghost yelled "Boo!" excitedly.

Decide if the words you underlined above are adjectives or adverbs. Write each word in the correct column.

Adjectives	Adverbs

     Advantage Reading Grade 5 © 2004 Creative Teaching Press

Invitations are cards or letters that invite people to special events. They usually tell the date, time, and location of the event as well as special instructions such as what to wear or what to bring. Read the following costume party invitation and then answer the questions on page 98.

You are invited to a COSTUME PARTY!
Join Michele and Tim at the farm for an evening of food, games, and laughs!

WHERE: 123 Hilltop Road, Haytown

WHEN: October 1st, 5:00 p.m.

Come ready for these fun-filled activities:
- Egg toss
- Square dancing
- Pie-eating contest
- Haunted hayrides
- Stuffing scarecrows
- Bobbing for apples
- Old-fashioned pig roast

WHAT TO BRING:

Old clothes to dress your scarecrow.

Come dressed to have fun!
Prizes for the most hilarious costumes!
Please RSVP by September 25th so we know how many pies to make!
(111-222-3333)

Reading: Comprehension

Fill in the bubble next to the correct answer.

1 This party will MOST likely take place during what season?

    Ⓐ fall

    Ⓑ spring

    Ⓒ winter

    Ⓓ summer

2 Which of these will probably NOT happen at the party?

    Ⓕ eating pies

    Ⓖ making scarecrows

    Ⓗ entering a baking contest

    Ⓙ riding behind a tractor

3 Which of these people would MOST likely win the costume contest?

    Ⓐ Julie dressed as a cat

    Ⓑ Dave dressed as a fairy

    Ⓒ Sarah dressed as a princess

    Ⓓ George dressed as a football player

4 What does "RSVP" most likely mean?

    Ⓕ Bring a pie.

    Ⓖ Tell a friend.

    Ⓗ Don't be late.

    Ⓙ Please respond.

5 How do you think the "egg toss" game will be played? What will people probably do with the eggs?

_____

_____

_____

 Advantage Reading Grade 5 © 2004 Creative Teaching Press

Legends are fictional stories that are passed down from generation to generation. Some legends are about an imaginary creature or a person with extraordinary powers or strength. Other legends have animals as characters. Legends often try to explain natural occurrences. Read the following legend and then answer the questions on page 102.

Campfire Storytime

"The fire is really blazing now, Dad," Tammy told her father.

Mr. Williams smiled at his daughter and asked, "Shall I take out the marshmallows now, girls?"

"Yeah!" the three girls shouted in unison.

"This is the best campfire party I've ever been to!" Maria said. "Hey, Mr. Williams, what are you going to wear to the neighborhood costume party this year? Everyone thought your superhero costume last year was hilarious!"

As he reached out to put a marshmallow on a long stick, Mr. Williams responded, "This year I'll have the scariest costume at the party."

"A devil?" asked Tamika.

Mr. Williams shook his head back and forth. "No. Guess again."

"A werewolf?" asked Maria.

"No. Give up?" he replied.

"Oh, Dad, just tell them. He's going to be Bigfoot. Real scary, huh?" Tammy reported in a sarcastic voice, as she covered a fake yawn with her hand.

Mr. Williams corrected her. "His real name is Sasquatch. Bigfoot is just a name that people who have never heard the legend call him."

"Legend?" Tammy glanced at her father.

"What is the legend?" Tamika asked.

"Go on. Tell us the legend of Sasquatch, Mr. Williams," pleaded Maria.

Mr. Williams sat among the girls and asked, "Does everyone have enough marshmallows?" He went on, "Here's how the story goes."

The Legend of Sasquatch

There have been many sightings of Sasquatch over the years. He has been spotted in Canada as well as in many regions of the Pacific Northwest in America. All the descriptions of the creature are remarkably similar: a hairy, ape-like, beast that stands between seven to nine feet tall and weighs between 500 and 900 pounds.

The first sighting of a Sasquatch by a man came in 1811 near what now is the town of Jasper in Canada. A trader named David Thompson found some strange footprints, fourteen inches long and eight inches wide, with four toes, in the snow.

Then in 1884 the newspaper *Daily Colonist*, of Victoria, British Columbia, reported that a train crew had captured a creature resembling Sasquatch. The creature was spotted along the Fraser River. The crew stopped the train and chased and captured the animal after following it up a rocky hill. The creature was described as ". . . something of the gorilla type . . . with long black, hair and resembles a human being with one exception; his entire body, except his hands (or paws) and feet are covered with glossy hair about one inch long . . . he possesses extraordinary strength, as he will take hold of a stick and break it by wrenching it or twisting it, which no man could break in the same way."

Rumors about Sasquatch continued through the end of the century. Then, in 1910, two miners were found with their heads cut off. The murder was attributed to the creature. The place of the murders, Nahanni Valley, in Canada, was changed to Headless Valley, because of the incident.

In 1924, around the Mount St. Helens area, a man complained to a forest ranger that he'd been woken up in the middle of the night. He said that stones were thrown at his cabin. Peeking outside, he saw several Sasquatches "screaming like a bunch of apes." The man hid under his bed all night. The next morning, he found the cabin surrounded by giant footprints.

Sasquatch footprints were discovered again in 1958. A bulldozer operator named Jerry Crew was working in Humboldt County, California, when he spotted an enormous footprint sunken in the ground. The construction crew made a cast of the footprint. A local newspaper ran the story and included a photo of the footprint. The story ran in other papers throughout the country. It was the picture of the crew holding the cast that made the name "Bigfoot" stick in the minds of Americans.

The next sighting wouldn't be until many years later, in 1977. Two 13-year-old boys in Ohio told this story: "We were walking our dog and she got excited about something. She got away from us and I ran after her. When I picked her up, we smelled this awful stink, like rotten eggs. When my friend and I turned around, we saw this creature that was about 9 feet tall and weighed somewhere around 500 pounds. It had dirty brown hair and what looked like white eyes. Its arms were real long and hung almost to the ground. It chased us down by the bridge, across a soybean field toward my home. It seemed like it was right behind us, as it took very large steps. When we reached the railroad tracks and the highway, it vanished from our view." When the boys got home, they notified the local Sheriff's Department. The boys accompanied the sheriff to the scene. They refused to get out of the cruiser while the area was searched. For the next week, one of the boys refused to go out at night or even open his bedroom window.

People don't know where the Sasquatch came from or why he shows himself to people, but if you ask the Iroquois Native Americans of the Northeast, they'll tell you that there is a purpose for his visits. They claim that he is a messenger from the Creator trying to warn humans to change their ways or face disaster. In Native American culture, the entire natural world—the animals, the plants, the rivers, the stars—is thought to be part of the same family. The Sasquatch is seen as one of our close relatives, the "great elder brother."

Reading: Comprehension

Fill in the bubble next to the correct answer.

1 What is another name for Sasquatch?

    (A) Bigpaw   (C) Godzilla

    (B) Bigfoot   (D) Hairy Ape Man

2 According to the legend, where was the first sighting of Sasquatch?

    (F) Ohio   (H) Victoria

    (G) Jasper   (J) Humboldt County

3 Sasquatch is described as being _____.

    (A) hairless   (C) nine feet tall

    (B) 300 pounds   (D) sweet-smelling

4 According to the story, who believes that Sasquatch is a "great elder brother"?

    (F) Jerry Crew   (H) the Sheriff's Department

    (G) David Thompson   (J) the Iroquois

5 When you retell a story, you tell it to someone after you have read it or heard it. Choose one of the Sasquatch sightings described in the legend and retell it to a friend or sibling. Write his or her response on the lines below.

_____

_____

_____

_____

Details
Writing is full of details. Details are small facts and specific bits of information such as names, dates, and descriptions. Paying attention to details helps you to visualize and have a fuller understanding of what you are reading.

Graphic Information: Venn Diagram

Costume Party

Venn diagrams are used to compare and contrast information. They usually show 2 or 3 overlapping circles. What is the same about what is being compared can be found in the overlapping middle part of the Venn diagram. What is different can be found in the part of each circle that doesn't overlap. Study the Venn diagram below. Then answer the questions on page 104.

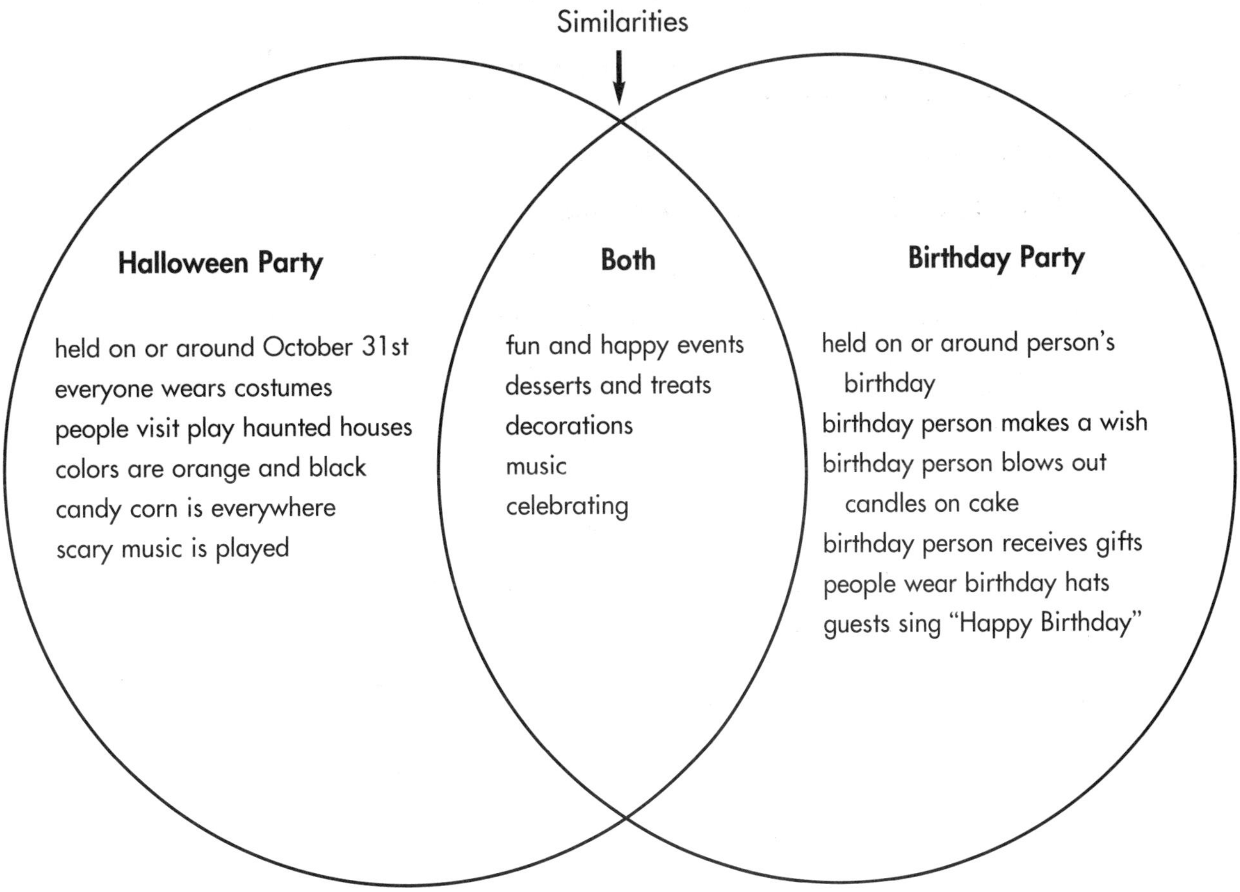

Similarities

Halloween Party

held on or around October 31st
everyone wears costumes
people visit play haunted houses
colors are orange and black
candy corn is everywhere
scary music is played

Both

fun and happy events
desserts and treats
decorations
music
celebrating

Birthday Party

held on or around person's
    birthday
birthday person makes a wish
birthday person blows out
    candles on cake
birthday person receives gifts
people wear birthday hats
guests sing "Happy Birthday"

Reading: Comprehension

Fill in the bubble next to the correct answer.

1 What is being compared in the Venn diagram?

    Ⓐ haunted houses to regular houses

    Ⓑ Halloween music to birthday music

    Ⓒ Halloween parties to birthday parties

    Ⓓ Halloween parties to Christmas parties

2 What is the same about both events?

    Ⓕ They both are fun and happy events.

    Ⓖ They both have guests wearing costumes.

    Ⓗ They both have orange and black balloons.

    Ⓙ They both have someone who blows out cake candles.

3 Which of these statements is true?

    Ⓐ Halloween parties are always held on October 31st.

    Ⓑ Everyone wears a scary costume to Halloween parties.

    Ⓒ Candy corn is everywhere at Halloween parties.

    Ⓓ Halloween parties are usually held inside of a haunted house.

4 What is different about a Halloween party?

    Ⓕ Cake is usually served.

    Ⓖ People usually bring gifts.

    Ⓗ Guests wear orange and black.

    Ⓙ Scary music is played.

5 Which of these statements is true?

    Ⓐ Birthday cakes are usually orange and black.

    Ⓑ At birthday parties, some people wear birthday hats.

    Ⓒ The birthday person sings "Happy Birthday" to the guests.

    Ⓓ Birthday guests dress up as ghosts, devils, witches, and monsters.

Costume Party

Writing: How-To Guide

⭐ When a writer wants to explain how to do something such as operate a toy or fix a broken machine, he or she writes a "how-to guide." These guides usually include steps to take or procedures to do. Write a how-to guide that will teach people how to throw a successful costume party. Read the following ideas and add to the list using the graphic organizer below.

Design colorful invitations and mail or hand them out at least two weeks early.

Have a costume contest with funny prizes for the winners.

Costume Party

Writing: How-To Guide

⭐ Write your how-to guide using the ideas you listed on page 105.
Remember these important points when writing:
• Keep your directions clear and concise.
• Write your steps in the order in which they should be done and
  number the steps.

_____

_____

_____

_____

_____

_____

_____

_____

_____

_____

_____

_____

_____

_____

_____

Word Practice

Keep a list of words that have double vowels. When you have at least 25 words, separate them into two lists. One list can be one-syllable words (VV). Another list can be words with two or more syllables. Decide if there is a syllable division in between the vowels. Then divide them using the V/V syllabication rule.

Speech Practice

Design an invitation to a sleep-over pajama party. Be sure to include important information such as your address, the date and time of the party, and what guests should bring. Think of fun activities for you and your friends to do and write them into the invitation. Draw balloons and party favors on the outside of the invitation.

Scrapbook

Write a telephone conversation skit or use the one on page 93. Invite a friend over. Have your friend be one character and you can be the other. Each of you can hold a banana up to one ear and talk into it like a telephone receiver. Read your lines, varying your intonation to express emotion.

Make a Mask

Make a mask for a Halloween costume. Mix ingredients needed to make paper maché. Tear up strips of old newspaper. Blow up a balloon until it is about the size of your head. Dunk a strip of newspaper into the paper maché mix and mold it onto one side of the balloon. Keep doing this until you have created an oval-shaped mask. Let it dry overnight. Cut eye holes in the mask. Decorate your mask with acrylic paint, feathers, and glitter.

Check out these books.

Costumes: Traditions Around the World by Danielle Sensier (Thomson Learning)

The Halloween Costume Party by Ronald Wegen (Houghton Mifflin)

Halloween Fun for Everyone by Ferida Wolff (Beech Tree Books)

Party Secrets: Who to Invite, Most-Loved Munchies, Must-Dance Music & Foolproof Fun by Sarah Jane Brian (Pleasant Company Publications)

Scary Halloween Costume Book by Carol Barkin (William Morrow)

Super Slumber Parties by Brooks Whitney (Pleasant Company Publications)

Page 5
Answers will vary depending on what students know about the three branches of government.

Page 6
1 witness
2 pumpkin
3 inspect
4 shipment
5 plastic
6 complete
7 tadpole
8 vampire
9 tarnish
10 blissful
11 argument
12 afternoon
13 compensate
14 memorize
15 maximize

Page 7
1 hun/dred
2 chil/dren
3 sam/ple
4 dis/cuss
5 sand/wich
6 bot/tom
7 flan/nel
8 an/nex
9 cot/ton
10 sud/den

Page 8
The following 14 two-syllable words can be in any order.
1 sig/nal
2 bas/ket
3 mag/net
4 gar/lic
5 zip/per
6 per/son
7 con/sent
8 con/test
9 pub/lic
10 gob/let
11 pan/cake
12 ab/sent
13 un/til
14 mut/ter

The following six three-syllable words can be in any order.
15 im/por/tant
16 fan/tas/tic
17 il/lus/trate
18 in/ter/rupt

19 car/pen/ter
20 in/for/mal

Page 9
1 kidnap
2 cactus
3 verdict
4 chapter
5 establish
6 turpentine
7 different
8 interfere
9 letter
10 gallop
11 attic
12 tennis
13 muffin
14 kitten
15 button
16 fossil
17 gallon

Page 11
1 Answers will vary. A correct answer will identify paragraph 2, 3, 4, or 5.
2 Responses will vary. Acceptable answers should state the meaning of the paragraph written for question number 1 above.
3 Correct responses will refer to Martin Luther King's dream and hope that someday all people, no matter what race or ethnicity, will be treated fairly and equally.

Page 12
1 lay
2 has laid
3 lie
4 has lain
5 laid
6 is laying

Page 13
1 bill
2 politician
3 immigrant
4 citizen
5 veto

```
V A P (I M M I G R A N T) T O S C T I O N
I M O B I L I B (C) E W I N S O T P A G E
G V D H I (P O L I T I C I A N) T H O B I
C E T I (C O N S T I T U T I O N) T E I O
R T S T I O N M I A G R A N T O P I L V
L O Z E N L A P Z E M B I O P L A C L T
H O V E O T I Z E N M S P A F S H I N G
G R E A H M E R N E T R O B L B E N E L
```

Page 15
1 D
2 F
3 D
4 J
5 C

Page 19
1 A
2 D
3 C
4 K
5 B
6 L
7 E
8 J
9 G
10 M
11 H
12 A
13 F
14 I

Page 20
Constitution
Congress
House of Representatives
Senate
President
Vice President
President
Supreme Court
Constitution
Federal Courts
State Courts

Page 22
The topic should be a citizen right or responsibility. The essay should have an introductory paragraph that states a position. The body of the essay should have three paragraphs, each with supportive reasoning. Each paragraph should also include at least one supporting example, fact, or piece of evidence. The conclusion should restate the original position and the most compelling reason.

Page 24
Answers should accurately reflect the information in the diagram of the Earth's interior.

Page 25
1 mu/sic
2 tu/lip
3 i/vy
4 de/cide

5 ba/con
6 pa/per
7 tro/phy
8 ivy
9 bacon
10 trophy
11 tulip
12 paper
13 decide

Page 26
1 cam/el
2 men/u
3 fin/ish
4 lem/on
5 stud/y
6 nov/el
7 menu
8 novel
9 lemon
10 finish
11 study
12 camel

Page 27
The following ten V/CV words can be in any order.
1 pō/lo
2 mē/ter
3 rā/ven
4 lē/gal
5 bō/nus
6 pō/ny
7 rē/cent
8 vī/tal
9 tō/tal
10 vā/cant

The following ten VC/V words can be in any order.
11 pôl/ish
12 mê/tal
13 râd/ish
14 lêv/el
15 bôd/y
16 pûn/ish
17 rêl/ish
18 vîv/id
19 tôn/ic
20 vân/ish

Page 28
1 punish
2 present
3 credit
4 clever
5 raven
6 spider

7 student
8 sinus

Page 30
For the "same" category, the answers should mention that they are all parts of the Earth. For the "different" category, answers will vary. Some possible answers will refer to temperature, miles of thickness, chemical makeup, solid or liquid core, and other facts from "Earth Rap."

1 The rap compares the Earth to a peach.
2 In paragraph 2, the outer crust is compared to the skin of the peach.
3 In paragraph 3, the mantle is compared to the meat of the peach.
4 In paragraph 4, the outer core is compared to the pit of the peach.
5 In paragraph 5, the inner core is compared to a seed inside the pit of a peach.

Page 31
1 sit
2 set
3 has sat
4 sat
5 has set
6 set

Page 32
```
P S P I R M A N T L E C E P S S A T G O N S L O P
K F O B I L I B C E W I N S O T P A L E T M A K O
G O D H I E R U P T I O N T H O C I L Y I S V R V
C S T C I E R S T L A V T I N T O E C O P L A T E
R S H T I O N M I A G E O T H E R M A L F S S I L
L I Z N L A P Z E M I R O P L I E K T O S T I O N
H U V E C T I Z E N M O P A F S H I R A G Y U T L
G E O L R A P H Y E I S O B L B E N G L A C I E R
H L I E U T I Z P N M I I A F S H Y O M O P I E R
A L V E S T A Z E G E O L O G Y H I R A G Y U F J
C G F X T D I S U N M N P A C R A T E R O N L S K
```

Page 35
Answers will vary. Possible predictions will take into account the events that occurred at the beginning and middle of the story.

Page 37
MAIN CHARACTER—Answer should mention Jazzy, a middle-school-aged girl.
SETTING—Answer should mention a lake-front property near Mount St. Helens.
PROBLEM—Answer should mention that a family is evacuating the area where Mount St. Helens is erupting, but that they left the family dog behind.
SOLUTION—Answer should mention that the dog was safe after all; he was hiding in the upstairs bedroom.

Page 39
1 The sky is filled with ash, sulfur, and other substances from the eruption.
2 John kept his airline tickets as a souvenir and to help him remember what he saw.
3 Fiction
   Correct answers will include science fiction facts from the story such as flying houses.
4 Nonfiction
   Correct answers will say that the article is based on a true eyewitness account.

Page 40
1 A
2 H
3 D
4 G

Page 41
Earth
outer crust
mantle
outer core
inner core

Page 45
Answers on the CD rack labels will include musical genres such as folk, pop, rock and roll, blues, country, hip-hop, new age, and heavy metal.

Page 46
The following 10 words can be in any order.
1 join
2 zip
3 map
4 beg
5 tan
6 swim
7 dab
8 cram
9 stub
10 pin

Page 47
1 election
2 neighborhood
3 kindness
4 fishing
5 handsome

Page 48

1 n running
2 g jogger
3 n thinnest
4 p dropping
5 p slipped
6 n sunny
7 n spinning
8 d maddest
9 d reddish
10 d sadder
11 n funny
12 g begged
13 t flattest

Page 49

1 nabbed
2 rusty
3 stopping
4 sluggish
5 lonely
6 painting
7 sinner
8 tilted
9 sadness
10 biggest
11 Susan gladly wrapped the wedding gift.
12 Frank dropped the glass when the cat jumped.
13 The furry animal went swimming in the pond.
14 Josh looked for a romantic table under the dimmest lights.
15 The Scottish doctor looked at her painful leg.
16 The Big Dipper is the brightest star tonight.

Page 51

1 C
2 J
3 red
4 cat
5 hand
6 three
7 dad

Page 52

1 raise
2 raised
3 has risen
4 rose
5 rises
6 has raised

Page 53

1 tempo
2 lyrics
3 orchestra
4 note
5 conductor
6 opera
7 melody
8 beat
9 compose
10 instrument

Page 57

Answers will vary. Possible predictions will take into account the events that occurred at the beginning and middle of the story.

Page 59

1 The story is mainly about a boy who has to make a decision about friendship.
2 G
3 The story is called *A Lesson on Friendship* because Trevor learned that true friends don't ask each other to steal for them. Friends look out for each other.
4 F
5 D

Page 61

1 D
2 Some singers and musicians think that downloading music is like free advertising. It helps promote their music. Other singers and musicians think that downloading music isn't right because people don't have to buy entire albums. Then they don't get to listen to the less popular songs.
3 D
4 F

Page 63

1 C
2 G
3 D
4 An acceptable answer will explain an alternative but possible avenue that Tommy could have taken to meet his goal of becoming a famous singer. For example, he could have been "discovered" at a talent show.

Page 64

The Problem/Solution Story Planner should be completely filled out. In the Problem section, it should say that the record store is losing business.

Page 68

1 dle cradle
2 ble table
3 tle battle
4 fle rifle
5 kle sparkle
6 ble marble
7 tle settle
8 fle ruffle
9 dle huddle
10 kle buckle
11 tle rattle
12 dle handle
13 ble fable
14 ble stable
15 tle cattle
16 dle paddle
17 kle tackle
18 tle gentle
19 tle startle
20 ble cable

Page 69

1 bu/gle
2 i/dle
3 stum/ble
4 brit/tle
5 twin/kle
6 poo/dle
7 ma/ple
8 cir/cle
9 an/kle
10 no/ble
11 raf/fle
12 gur/gle
13 bri/dle
14 un/cle
15 puz/zle

Page 70

1 twinkle, settled
2 stumbled, ankle
3 gentle, poodle
4 eagle, maple
5 gurgled, bottle
6 saddle, stable.
7 purple, sparkled
8 middle, table
9 Words with **ble:** stumbled, stable, table
10 Words with **ple:** purple, maple
11 Words with **tle:** bottle, settled, gentle
12 Words with **gle:** eagle, gurgled
13 Words with **kle:** twinkle, ankle, sparkled
14 Words with **dle:** saddle, poodle, middle

Advantage Reading Grade 5 © 2004 Creative Teaching Press

Page 71
1 eagle
2 buckle
3 ruffle
4 candle
5 kettle
6 tickle
7 tremble
8 raffle
9 bundle
10 muscle
11 noble
12 huddle
13 castle
14 puzzle
15 temple
16 humble
17 cradle
18 rattle
19 uncle
20 baffle
21 obstacle
22 example
23 icicle
24 particle
25 miracle
26 barnacle

Page 73
1 B
2 F
3 a wind storm
4 a wet magazine
5 a fortress
6 an army

Page 74
1 except
2 accept
3 accept
4 except
5 accept
6 except
7 Sentences will vary but should include correct use of the word *accept*.
8 Sentences will vary but should include correct use of the word *except*.

Page 75
1 anthropology = the study of man
2 biology = the study of life
3 geology = the study of the earth
4 neurology = the study of nerves
5 zoology = the study of animals
6 entomology = the study of insects

Page 77
1 D
2 F
3 C
4 G
5 Answers will vary. Any answer that seems probable based on the student's prior knowledge about volcanoes is acceptable.

Page 82
1 A
2 H
3 D
4 J
5 Liz was bothered by Tommy at the beginning because he talked too much. At the end, she was glad to have him nearby because he knew so much. In the dungeon, she thought she would choose him if she had to pick someone to be stuck there with.

Page 84
1 B
2 F
3 D
4 G
5 C

Page 85
Answers will vary according to results. The writing in the oval should describe the effect or outcome of the experiment—what happened (red "lava" will flow out if done correctly). The writing in the rectangle should describe a possible cause for the effect—why the student thinks it happened.

Page 86
The journal article should compare the effects of the experiment to what happens in a real volcano. Responses will vary. Here is the true scientific explanation/theory: Mixing baking soda and vinegar produces a chemical reaction in which carbon dioxide gas is created the same gas that comes from a real volcano. The gas bubbles build in the bottle, forcing the "lava" mixture out of the bottle and down the sides.

Page 89
1 po/et
2 tru/ant
3 di/et
4 flu/id
5 sci/ence
6 re/act
7 du/al
8 me/ow
9 mu/se/um
10 nu/cle/us
11 o/a/sis
12 vi/o/lin
13 me/te/or
14 cha/ot/ic
15 i/o/dine
16 co/in/cide

Page 90
1 et rock/et
2 et qui/et
3 et di/et
4 et du/et
5 et po/et
6 et midg/et
The following three words with *al* endings can be in any order.
7 trial
8 steal
9 dial
The following three words with *el* endings can be in any order.
10 fuel
11 duel
12 cruel
The following two words with *ant* endings can be in any order.
13 truant
14 giant
The following two words with *ent* endings can be in any order.
15 fluent
16 client

Page 91
The following nine one-syllable words (VV) can be in any order.
jail
preach
pie
paint
toe
suit
fruit
spoil
poach
The following nine two-syllable words (V/V) can be in any order.
cre/ate
li/on
sci/ence
tru/ant
po/em
di/al
re/act

ru/in
ne/on

1 fruit
2 dial
3 paint, neon
4 suit, ruin
5 spoil, pie

Page 92
1 triumph
2 diet
3 create
4 fluid
5 riot
6 cruel
7 violence
8 meander
9 oasis
10 pioneer
11 rodeo
12 nucleus
13 violin
14 iodine
15 minuet
16 influence

Page 94
1 A
2 H
3 D
4 F
5 C

Page 95
1 farther
2 further
3 farther
4 farther
5 further
6 further
7 Sentences will vary but should correctly use the word *farther*.
8 Sentences will vary but should correctly use the word *further*.

Page 96
1 She wore a colorful wig.
2 The guests quickly walked to the party.
3 She had a beautiful dress on.
4 The fur on his costume was fluffy.
5 I bravely walked into the room in my costume.
6 The skin on the mask looked wrinkled.
7 We waited patiently for the contest to begin.
8 The face on my friend's costume was scary.

9 Tim dressed as a lion and growled fiercely.
10 The person dressed as a ghost yelled "Boo!" excitedly.
The following five adjectives can be in any order.
colorful
beautiful
fluffy
wrinkled
scary
The following five adverbs can be in any order.
quickly
bravely
patiently
fiercely
excitedly

Page 98
1 A
2 H
3 B
4 J
5 Answers will vary. There should be some mention that guests will toss eggs to each other to see who keeps the egg the longest.

Page 102
1 B
2 G
3 C
4 J
5 Responses will vary. An accurate retelling of one of the sightings in the legend is acceptable and should lead to questions or feedback from the listener.

Page 104
1 C
2 F
3 C
4 J
5 B

Page 106
How-to guides will vary. They should list and number the ideas in the order they should be completed. The directions should be clear and concise.

Advantage Reading Grade 5 © 2004 Creative Teaching Press